Workbook for

Modern Carpentry

S0-ADU-286

Building Construction Details in Easy-to-Understand Form

by

WILLIS H. WAGNER
Professor Emeritus, Industrial Technology
University of Northern Iowa, Cedar Falls

and

HOWARD BUD SMITH
Author/Chief Editor
Lee Howard Associates
Bayfield, Wisconsin

Publisher
THE GOODHEART-WILLCOX COMPANY, INC.
Tinley Park, Illinois

Introduction

TO THE STUDENT:

This workbook has been prepared for use with the textbook, MODERN CARPENTRY. It is designed to help you in your study of carpentry. It will reinforce your understanding of the correct procedures and the vast amount of technical information connected with the trade.

The units in the workbook correlate with those in the textbook. The order of the individual questions and problems also follow the same sequence as the textbook material. This will make it easier for you to find information in the textbook when checking your answers.

To make this workbook a more effective guide to learning, it is suggested that you first study the assigned material in the textbook. As you study, pay close attention to both the text and the illustrations. The drawings and photographs contain a great deal of important information. Study each illustration and its caption carefully until you understand what it is conveying.

After you have completed the study assignment, lay the textbook aside while you study and answer the problems in the workbook. Note that the answers are to be entered in the blank spaces along the right-hand side of the page. Some answers will simply consist of letters and numbers while others require words. When filling in words, be sure they are spelled correctly. It is also advisable to print instead of using longhand. Many carpenters follow this practice in figures and notations because it is easier for others to read and it reduces the probability of errors.

As you work your way through each unit, fill in the blanks whenever you are relatively certain of the answer. Guessing is not really helpful in a learning activity. Use the text to find the answers for the questions that you missed. Check for correctness of your answers. Do not just copy the answer from the book. Be certain that you understand the principles, practices, or information relating to the answer. You may want to use a colored pencil for filling in these answers. By doing so, they may be easily identified as you study for a later review.

A number of the units in the workbook include problems in estimating amounts of material and other calculations. Work out the problem in the space provided so that your instructor can check your figures and determine if you have followed an efficient procedure. It will be best to list the steps in your calculations as shown in the textbook. Use the extra space on either side of this listing for adding, subtracting, and other arithmetic computations. Following this procedure will not only make it easier for your instructor to check your work, but will also keep you from becoming "lost" in complicated problems.

Limited space in the workbook restricts the number of material estimating problems included. Improving your abilities in this aspect of carpentry is very important. After solving those that are included, you may want to create and solve several of your own.

Willis H. Wagner
Howard Bud Smith

Contents

UNIT 1

Building Materials

Text pages 17-50

Name _____

Date _____ Score _____

1. The basic structure of wood consists of narrow tubes or cells held together with a natural substance called _____.

1. *fibers/tracheids*

2. Identify the basic parts of the tree trunk/log shown in the illustration below.

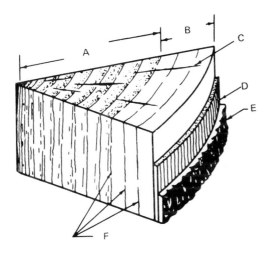

2. A. ♡ *wood*
   B. *SAP WOOD*
   C. *WOOD RAYS*
   D. *CAMBIUM*
   E. *BARK*
   F. *PITH*

3. Wood cells are formed in the _(A)_ layer. This growth occurs in the spring and summer, producing a layer of new cells each season. These layers are called _(B)_.

3. A. *Cambium*
   B. *Annular rings*

4. Softwood comes from the evergreen or needle-bearing trees. These trees are called _____ because many of them bear cones.

4. *Conifers*

5. Listed below are several kinds of commonly used hardwoods and softwoods. Select the four that are hardwoods and write them in the blanks provided.

H - ash *H*
H - basswood *H*
H - birch *S*
S - cypress *S*
S - Douglas fir *S*
hemlock - *S*
pine - *S*
redwood - *S*
spruce - *S*
willow - *H*

5. *ASH*
   WILLOW
   Basswood
   Birch

6. One kind of wood grown in the southeastern area of the United States is noted for its durability against decay. It is often used for exterior construction and interior wall paneling. Select the name from the list below and write it in the blank provided.

6. _____

    American elm   sycamore
    cypress   willow
    redwood   yellow poplar

7. When softwood lumber is cut so the annular rings form an angle of more than 45° with the surface of the board, the lumber is called ___D___.

7. _____

    A. quarter-sawed
    B. flat-grained
    C. plain-sawed
    D. edge-grained

8. What is the moisture content of a board if a test sample that originally weighed 8.5 oz. was found to weigh 7.4 oz. after oven drying? Round out your answer to the nearest percent. (Make your calculations in the space below.)

8. _____

9. For a 1% moisture loss below the fiber saturation point, wood will shrink (across the grain) about _____ in size.

9. _____

    A. 1/20
    B. 1/24
    C. 1/30
    D. 1/36

10. The average moisture content of interior woodwork installed in homes located in the midwestern United States is about _____.

10. _____

    A. 6%
    B. 8%
    C. 10%
    D. 12%

11. Two types of electrical moisture meters are the resistance type and the _____ type.

11. _____

12. Knots are caused by an embedded branch or limb of the tree. Identify the common types shown below.

12. A. _____

    B. _____

    C. _____

    D. _____

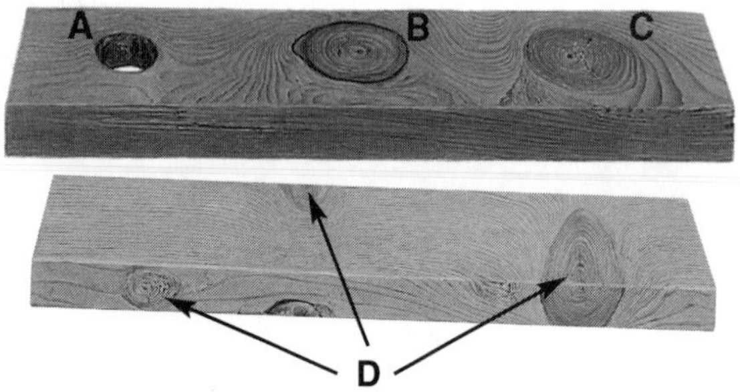

Name _____

13. Wood defects consisting of separation across the annular rings are called splits and checks. When the separation occurs between the annular rings, the defects are called.

13. _Shakes_

14. Any variation in a board from a true or plane surface is generally referred to as warp. Identify the specific kinds of warp illustrated below.

14. A. _Crook_
    B. _Bow_
    C. _Twist/wind_

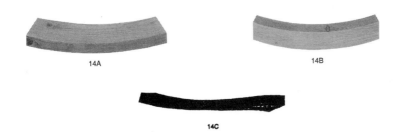

15. The three basic classifications of softwood lumber include boards, _____, and timbers.

15. _dimensional_

16. The best grade of pine boards generally available is designated as _____.

16. _____

17. The best grade of hardwood lumber normally available is identified by the letters _____.

17. _____

18. In the acronym, EMC, the E stands for _____.

18. _____

    A. elasticity
    B. equilateral
    C. equalized
    D. equilibrium

19. Rough lumber is surfaced and otherwise machined before it is used. Identify the width classifications in the view below.

19. A. _nominal_
    B. _dressed_
    C. _faced_

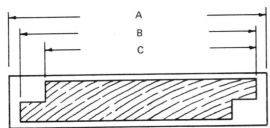

20. The actual width of a standard 2 × 8 piece of S4S framing lumber is _____.

20. _7 1/4_

    A. 7 1/4″
    B. 7 3/8″
    C. 7 1/2″
    D. 7 5/8″

21. A stack of 2 × 8s contains 21 pieces 16′ long, 12 pieces 14′ long, and 10 pieces 12′ long. What is the total bd. ft. of the stack? (Make your calculations in the space below.)

21. bd. ft. = _____

$$\frac{21 \times 2 \times 8 \times 16}{12}$$

$$\frac{12 \times 14 \times 2 \times 6}{12}$$

22. The illustration below shows a special kind of plywood panel. The core is made from oriented wood fibers glued together. The correct name for this kind of panel is _____ plywood.

22. _____

23. Species (kinds) of softwood used in making plywood manufacturing are classified in five groups. Group 1 represents the highest level of stiffness. Which one of the following is included in this group?

23. _____

 A. Redwood.
 B. Southern pine.
 C. Spruce.
 D. Western hemlock.

24. Hardboard is made from refined wood fibers held together with a natural cement called lignin. It is available in thicknesses up to _____.

24. _____

 A. 1/4″
 B. 5/16″
 C. 1/2″
 D. 5/8″

25. Particleboard is made from flakes, chips, and shavings bonded together with adhesives. Average panels consist of a density that results in a weight of _____ per cu. ft.

25. _____

 A. 35 lb.
 B. 40 lb.
 C. 45 lb.
 D. 50 lb.

Name _____

26. Nails are the most commonly used metal fastener. Identify the basic types shown below.

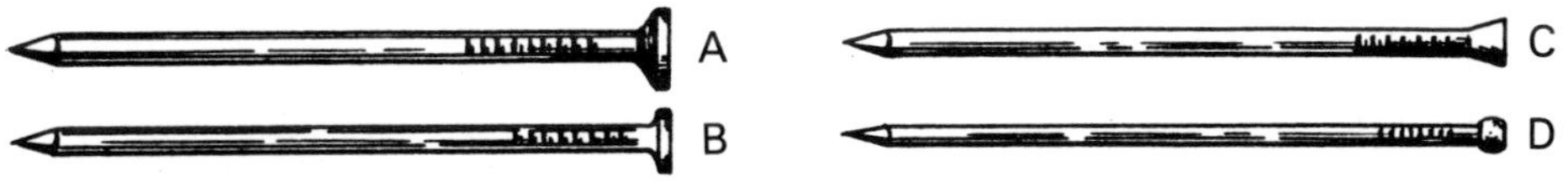

A

B

C

D

26. A. _Common_

    B. _box_

    C. _Casing_

    D. _finish_

27. What is the length of a 16d nail?

    A. 3″
    B. 3 1/4″
    C. 3 1/2″
    D. 3 3/4″

27. _C_

28. Wood screws have greater holding power than nails. Identify the three standard types of slotted screws shown below.

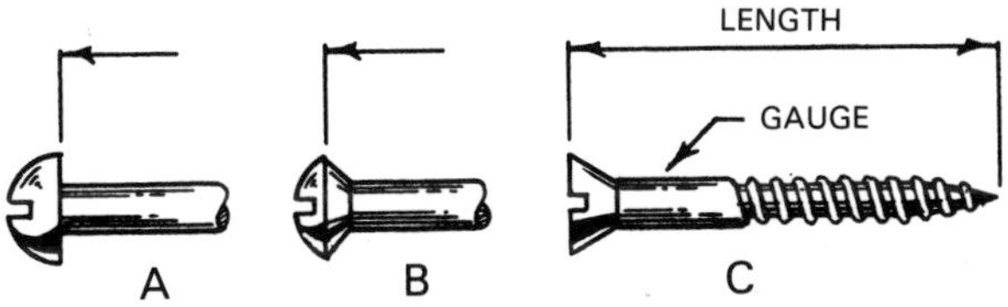

LENGTH

GAUGE

A   B   C

28. A. _____

    B. _____

    C. _____

29. Plastic laminates are usually applied with an adhesive called _____.

    A. contact cement
    B. polyvinyl glue
    C. casein glue
    D. urea cement

29. _____

30. Polyvinyl resin emulsion glue can be used to assemble a cabinet drawer. Which one of the following statements is *incorrect* concerning the characteristics of this kind of glue.

    A. The resin material used in the glue is thermoplastic.
    B. The glue has a high resistance to moisture.
    C. The glue is available in ready-to-use form.
    D. The glue sets up rapidly and does not stain the wood.

30. _____

31. Note the illustration of an APA trademark and indicate the meaning of each item designated with a letter. Place your answers in the appropriate spaces provided at the right.

31. A. _____

    B. _____

    C. _____

    D. _____

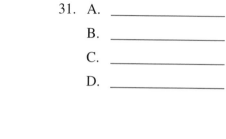

32. _____ _____ is a plywood strength rating and indicates the greatest recommended center-to-center distance in inches between supports when the long dimension of the panel is at right angles to the supports.

32. _____

33. The prefabricated structural unit indicated by the arrow is known as a(n) _____ _____.

33. _____

Name _____

34. Steel studs, shown below, can be fabricated in lengths up to _____'.

34. _____

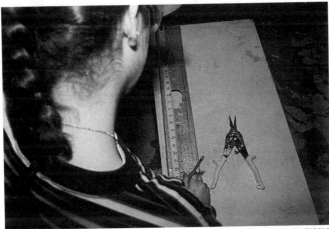

DES MOINES, IOWA PUBLIC SCHOOLS

35. Metal frame reinforcing units, shown below, are called anchors, strapping, or ties. What is their purpose and in what regions is their use especially important?

_____

_____

_____

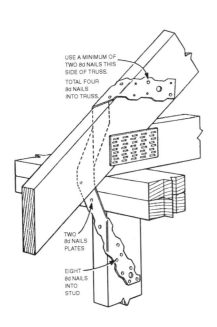

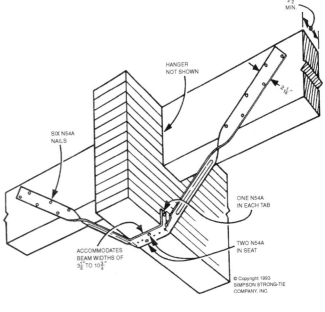

Modern Carpentry Workbook

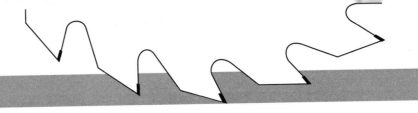

UNIT 2

General Safety Rules

Text Pages 51-54

Name _____

Date _____ Score _____

1. The two important factors in safety on the job are working _____ and following the _____.

   1. _____

2. _____ _____ shoes should never be used in carpentry; they have poor traction on smooth surfaces.

   2. _____

3. Standard specifications for lens in safety glasses state that they must withstand the impact of a _____.

   3. _____

   A. 1/16" diameter ball dropped from a height of 30'
   B. blow from a 16 oz. hammer
   C. 1/8" diameter ball dropped from a height of 50"
   D. 1" diameter ball dropped from a height of 30"

4. Hard hats must be able to resist denting from the force of a(n) _____ dropped from a height of _____.

   4. _____

   A. 8 lb. ball, 50"
   B. 80 lb. ball, 5'
   C. 80 oz. ball, 5'
   D. 1/8" diameter steel ball, 50"

5. Excavations can be shored up or sloped to their angle of repose. True or False?

5. _____

6. Scaffolds should be inspected every _____ for safe condition.

6. _____

   A. week
   B. day
   C. time erected
   D. month

7. Carpenters must have a good understanding of fire protection and control. For example, they should know that special methods must be used to control fires caused by electrical wiring or equipment. This type of fire is referred to as a _____.

7. _____

   A. class A
   B. class B
   C. class C
   D. None of the above.

8. Dull tools are hazardous to use because _____ _____ must be applied to make them cut.

8. _____

9. In carpentry, good housekeeping refers to the _____ and good order of the construction site.

9. _____

10. Pressure-treated lumber requires _____ care in handling.

10. _____

   A. no additional
   B. special
   C. little

UNIT 3

Hand Tools

Text Pages 55-74

Name _____

Date _____ Score _____

1. The two basic measuring tools most often used by the carpenter are the _____ and the _____.

    folding wood rule   plumb bob
    long tape   flexible measuring tape
    marking gauge   try square

1. A. _____

   B. _____

2. In the illustration below, the measuring tool being used to mark a rafter is called a(n) _____ _____ or a(n) _____ _____.

2. _____

_____

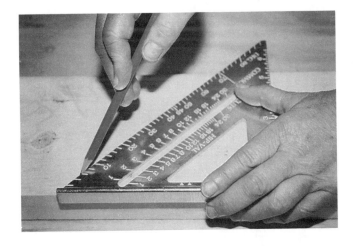

3. In the illustration below are three basic types of handsaws used by the carpenter. Correctly identify each saw.

3. A. _____

   B. _____

   C. _____

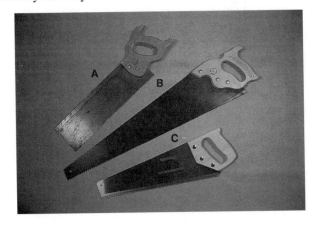

4. The tooth size of a handsaw is specified by listing the points per inch. How many teeth per inch will be found on an 8 point saw?

4. _____

5. The jack plane illustrated below is commonly selected for general purpose work. The bed of this plane is _____ long.

5. _____

    A. 8″ to 9″
    B. 10″
    C. 12″
    D. 14″

6. A small hand plane often used by the carpenter has a blade mounted at a low angle with the bevel of the cutter turned upward. The name of this plane is _____.

6. _____

7. Shown below is a special device used to guide a large backsaw. The carpenter uses it to make fine, accurate cuts. It is called a(n) _____.

7. _____

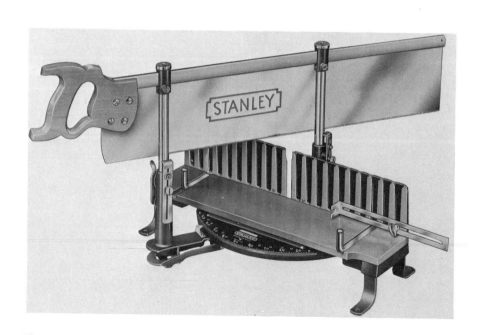

Name _____

8. An auger bit with the number "6" stamped on the tang or shank will bore a hole _____ in diameter.

    A. 1/4″
    B. 3/8″
    C. 1/2″
    D. 3/4″

8. _____

9. The hand tool used to turn auger bits, screwdriver bits, and countersinks is called a _____.

9. _____

10. A special type of boring bit that can be adjusted to produce holes of various sizes is called a(n) _____ bit.

10. _____

11. A tool, normally operated with one hand and commonly used by carpenters to form small holes, is called a(n) _____.

11. _____

12. Two shapes of hammer heads commonly used by the carpenter are the curved claw and the _____.

12. _____

13. Identify the parts of the standard claw hammer pictured below.

13. A. _____

    B. _____

    C. _____

    D. _____

    E. _____

    F. _____

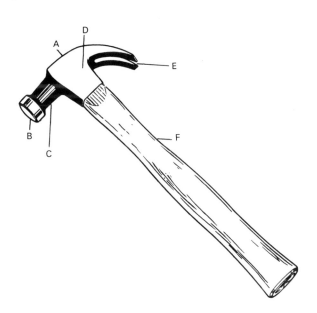

14. What type of striking tool is pictured below?

14. _____

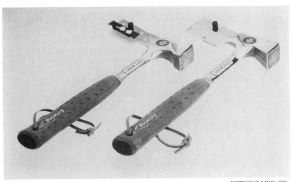

ESTWING MFG. CO.

15. Nail sets are about 4″ long. Size is determined by the diameter of the tip.
    Sizes vary by _____.   15. _____

    A. sixty-fourths
    B. thirty-seconds
    C. sixteenths
    D. eighths

16. Standard screwdriver size is determined by the length of the blade, measured
    from the tip to the _____.   16. _____

    A. ferrule
    B. handle
    C. head
    D. sleeve

17. Identify the three types of screwdrivers shown below.   17. A. _____

                                                          B. _____

                                                          C. _____

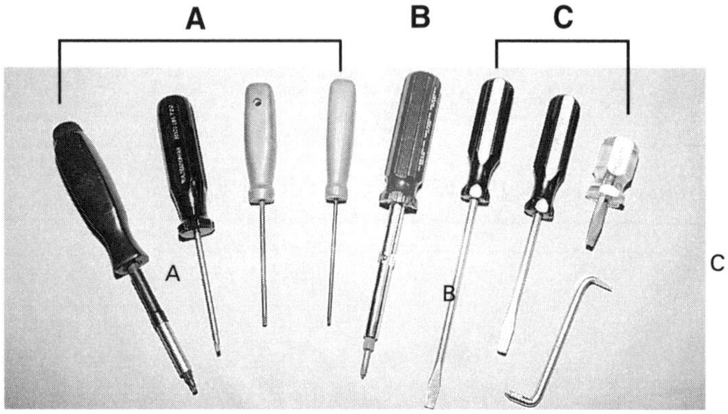

18. A standard clamping tool with wooden jaws is correctly called a _____.   18. _____

    A. hand screw
    B. joiner's clamp
    C. frame clamp
    D. C-clamp

19. The drawing below shows an edge view of a standard plane iron. Give the
    recommended angles for honing and grinding.   19. A. _____

                                                          B. _____

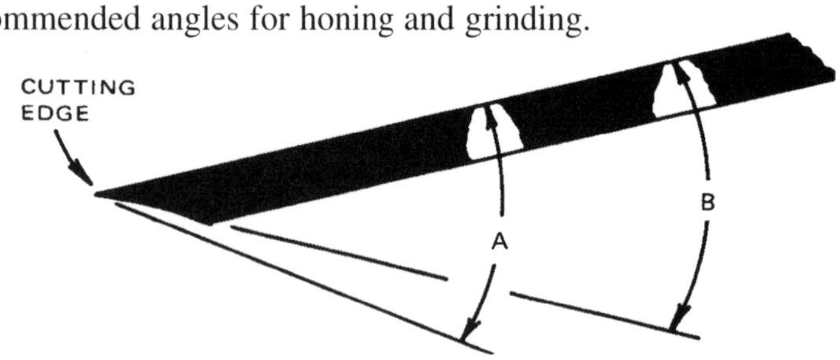

20. Auger bits are sharpened by filing the lips and spurs. Spurs should be filed
    on the _____ (inside, outside) only.   20. _____

21. _____ is a saw sharpening operation in which the points of the teeth are filed
    to equal height.   21. _____

    A. Leveling
    B. Striking
    C. Setting
    D. Jointing

Name _____

22. To save time when driving screws, the carpenter often uses a hand operated
tool like the one shown below. The correct name for this tool is _____.   22. _____

A. push drill
B. spiral ratchet screwdriver
C. ratchet drill and driver
D. automatic screwdriver

23. The name of a federal governmental agency that develops and administers
safety standards for business and industry is abbreviated with the letters
_____.   23. _____

A. SOHA
B. OSHA
C. AOSA
D. OSAH

24. The hand-held calculator shown below _____ (can, cannot) give answers in
SI metric.   24. _____

CALCULATED INDUSTRIES, INC.

Modern Carpentry Workbook

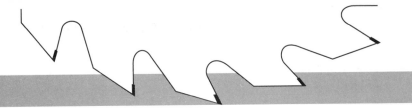

UNIT 4

Power Tools

Text Pages 75-100

Name _____

Date _____ Score _____

1. The two general types of power tools are portable and _____.

2. Electrical shock is one of the potential hazards in the operation of portable tools. In addition to using approved receptacles, plugs, and cords, always be sure that the tool is properly _____.

3. The illustration below shows portable power tools commonly used for carpentry. Write the name for each tool in the corresponding blank.

1. _____

2. _____

3. A. _____

   B. _____

   C. _____

   D. _____

   E. _____

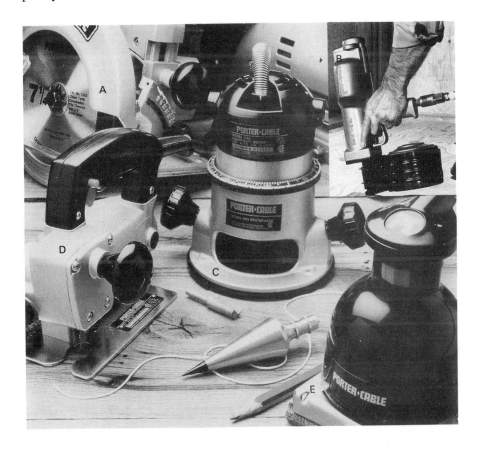

4. When using power tools, be sure the switch is in the _____ position before plugging it into the electrical outlet.

4. _____

5. The size of a portable circular saw is determined by the diameter of the largest blade that can be mounted on the arbor. Identify the specified parts of the model shown below.

5. A. _____

B. _____

C. _____

D. _____

E. _____

F. _____

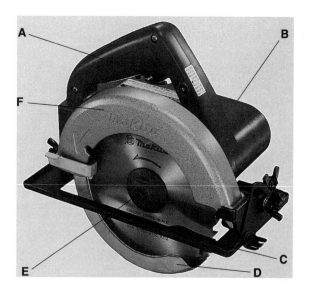

6. The depth of cut of the portable circular saw is adjusted by raising or lowering the base or _____.

6. _____

7. The depth of cut of the portable circular saw should be adjusted so the blade cuts through the stock and projects about _____.

A. 1/8″
B. 1/4″
C. 3/8″
D. 1/2″

7. _____

8. The following standard types of blades may be used on portable circular saws. Write the name for each type in the corresponding blank.

8. A. _____

B. _____

C. _____

D. _____

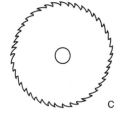
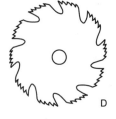

A   B   C   D

9. In the view below, a saber saw is being used to cut a hole in the subfloor for a plumbing fixture. The blade cuts on the _____ (upward, downward) stroke.

9. _____

Name _____

10. The length of stroke of a saber saw blade is about _____.   10. _____

    A. 1/4″
    B. 1/2″
    C. 3/4″
    D. 1″

11. The size of a portable electric drill is determined by the _____.   11. _____

    A. horsepower of the motor
    B. highest rpm capability
    C. capacity of the chuck
    D. length of the drill body

12. Which of the following is *not* a valid safety rule for the portable electric drill?   12. _____

    A. Stock to be drilled must be held in a stationary position.
    B. Place base of drill firmly on stock before starting motor.
    C. When drilling deep holes with a twist drill, withdraw drill several times to clear cuttings.
    D. Always remove drill bit from chuck as soon as you have completed your work.

13. The power plane motor drives a spiral cutter at speeds of about _____.   13. _____

    A. 5000 rpm
    B. 10,000 rpm
    C. 15,000 rpm
    D. 20,000 rpm

14. The depth of cut of a power plane is adjusted by raising or lowering the _____.   14. _____

    A. front shoe
    B. rear base
    C. cutterhead
    D. motor assembly

15. _____ bits for the router are used to cut dadoes and grooves.   15. _____

16. When viewed from above, a router motor revolves in a _____ (clockwise, counterclockwise) direction.   16. _____

17. The size of portable belt sanders, like the one shown below, is determined by the _____.   17. _____

    A. overall width
    B. belt width
    C. overall length
    D. motor hp

18. The nailer shown below uses _____ to drive regular nails.   18. _____

    A. electricity
    B. compressed air

19. To adjust the depth of cut of a standard radial arm saw, the _____ is raised or lowered.   19. _____

    A. table base
    B. motor mounting
    C. overhead arm
    D. vertical column

Name _____

20. The drawing below shows a standard setup for crosscutting with the radial arm saw. Identify the parts, thrust direction, and saw feed.

20. A. _____
    B. _____
    C. _____
    D. _____
    E. _____

21. Safety rules listed in the text prescribe a _____ margin of safety when operating the radial arm saw.

21. _____

    A. 2″
    B. 4″
    C. 6″
    D. 8″

22. When performing ripping operations on the radial arm saw, always feed the stock into the blade so that the bottom teeth are turning _____ (toward, away from) you.

22. _____

23. Identify the specified parts of the standard tilting arbor table saw illustrated below.

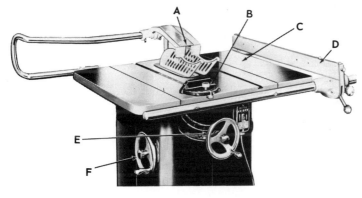

23. A. _____
    B. _____
    C. _____
    D. _____
    E. _____
    F. _____

24. Which of the following is *not* a valid safety rule for operating a standard table saw?

24. _____

    A. Set the blade so it extends 1/4″ above the stock to be cut.
    B. When ripping stock freehand, do not use the fence.
    C. Always use push sticks when ripping short, narrow pieces.
    D. Maintain a 4″ margin of safety even when the guard is in position.

25. Identify the specified parts of the standard jointer illustrated below.

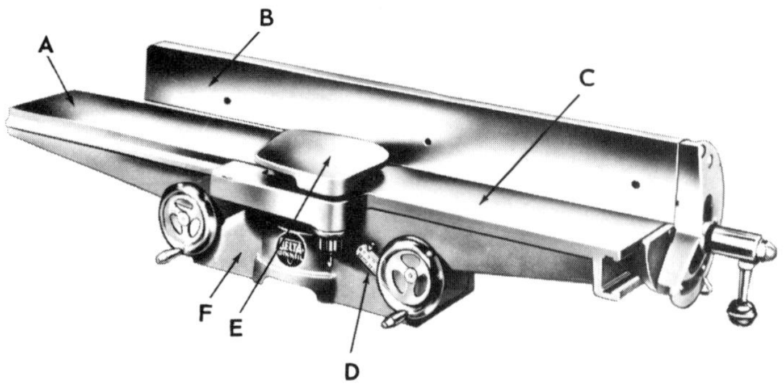

25. A. _____
    B. _____
    C. _____
    D. _____
    E. _____
    F. _____

26. When jointing the edge of a straight piece of stock, the depth of cut will gradually decrease (forming a taper) if the _____ .

    A. cutterhead is adjusted too high
    B. outfeed table is slightly higher than the cutterhead
    C. infeed table is too low
    D. outfeed table is lower than the infeed table

26. _____

27. Chains for chain saws come in lengths from about _____ ″ to _____ ″.

27. _____

28. The tool illustrated below, designed to attach drywall with screws, is known as a _____ _____.

28. _____

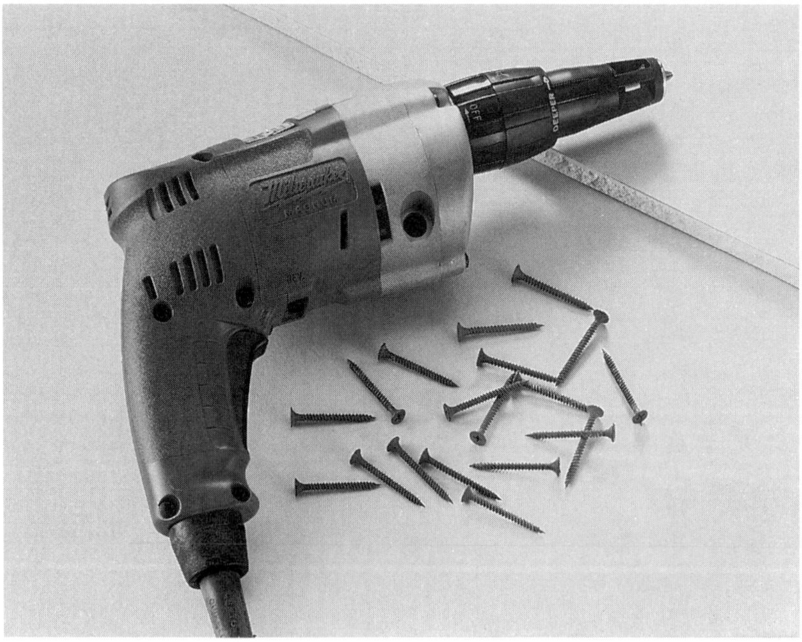

29. A _____ _____ is a portable tool designed for cutting slots in the edges of lumber for wood plates or biscuits.

29. _____

UNIT 5

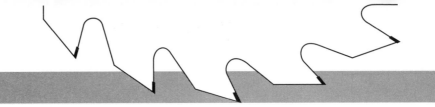

Leveling Instruments

Text Pages 101-113

Name _____

Date _____ Score _____

1. The operation of leveling instruments is based on the fact that a line of sight is always a _____ line.

   1. _____

2. Which of the following operations *cannot* be performed with a standard builders' level?

   2. _____

     A. Checking plumb lines.
     B. Laying out horizontal angles.
     C. Measuring horizontal angles.
     D. Laying out level lines.

3. Identify the parts of the standard builders' level shown below.

   3. A. _____

      B. _____

      C. _____

      D. _____

      E. _____

      F. _____

4. When in use, the level-transit must be securely mounted on a _____.

   4. _____

     A. transit stand
     B. leveling rod
     C. tripod
     D. rod base

5. In regular surveying work, both vertical and horizontal measurements are based on the foot and _____.

   5. _____

     A. decimal parts of an inch
     B. decimal parts of a foot
     C. fractional parts of a foot
     D. fractional parts of an inch

6. Two standard types of measuring tapes are shown in the illustration below. What is the reading designated at A and B?

6. A. _____

B. _____

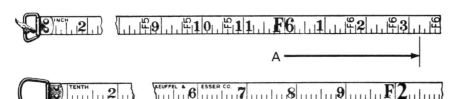

7. The view below shows how the leveling screws are adjusted on a standard instrument. With the screws being turned as indicated by the arrows, will the bubble move in the direction shown in A or the direction shown in B?

7. _____

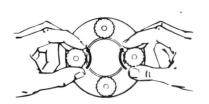

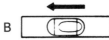

8. An officially established elevation that can be used for various building sites in a given area is called a(n) _____.

8. _____

9. The view below shows a builders' level positioned in two locations on a steep slope. With rod readings as given, what is the total difference in elevation between A and C? (Make your calculations in the space below.)

9. _____

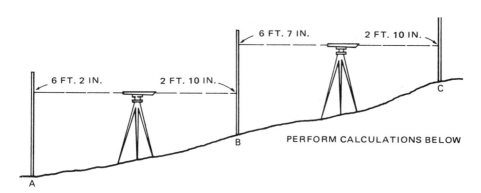

6 FT. 7 IN.   2 FT. 10 IN.

6 FT. 2 IN.   2 FT. 10 IN.

PERFORM CALCULATIONS BELOW

10. A drawing that shows the exact location of a building on a specific property (land area) is called a _____ plan.

10. _____

Name _____

11. When laying out squares or rectangles with the builders' level or level-transit, the instrument will need to be positioned at a minimum of _____.

    A. one corner
    B. two corners
    C. three corners
    D. four corners

11. _____

12. The Vernier scale is used to lay out or measure angles that include fractions of a degree. What is the exact angle shown below?

12. _____

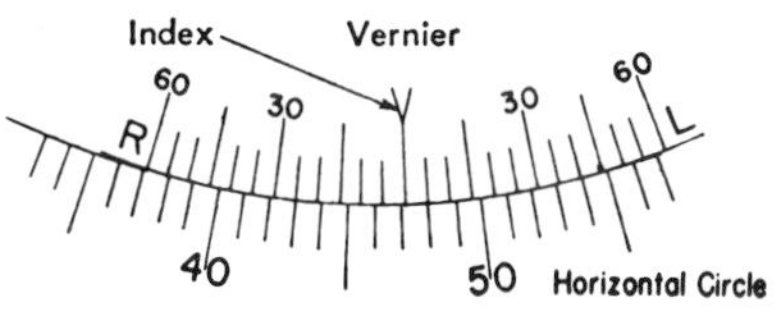

13. How many minutes in a complete circle? How many seconds in an angle of 15°? Use space below for calculations.

13. Minutes: _____

       Seconds: _____

14. Lines on a map or plot plan that run through points of an equal level or elevation are called _____.

14. _____

15. When setting a line of stakes on a slope, the _____ (builders' level, level-transit) would be the most efficient instrument to use.

15. _____

16. When sighting through the telescope of a leveling instrument, it is recommended that _____.

    A. one eye be kept closed
    B. both eyes be kept open

16. _____

17. Look at the illustration below. Explain how attaching a laserplane receiver to an excavating machine can speed up excavating.

_____

_____

_____

_____

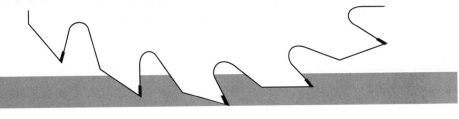

UNIT 6

Plans, Specifications, and Codes

Text Pages 115-139

Name _____

Date _____ Score _____

1. From the roof framing plan below, provide the following information:

    A. Sizes of rafters.
    B. Furring material used on some rafters.
    C. Spacing of rafters.
    D. Dimension of ridge boards.
    E. Use of 2 × 4s.
    F. Support material used under furred rafters.
    G. What "LVL" stands for.
    H. Spacing of collar ties.

1. A. _____
   B. _____
   C. _____
   D. _____
   E. _____
   F. _____
   G. _____
   H. _____

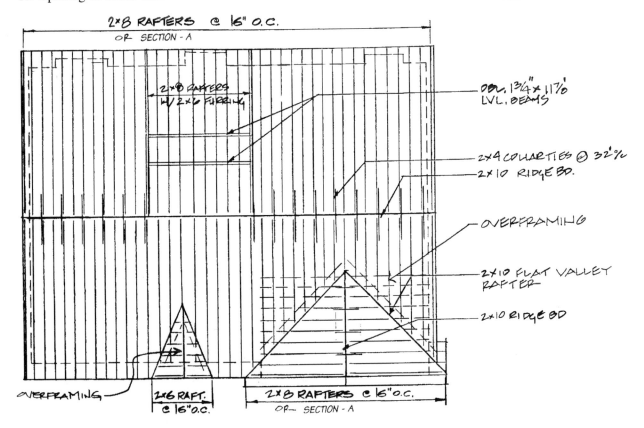

ROOF FRAMING PLAN
1/8" = 1'-0"

2. Study the floor plan shown below and provide the following information:

    A. Overall length of left wall.
    B. Width of front stoop concrete slab.
    C. Total number of hose bibs shown.
    D. Distance of bath window from nearest corner.
    E. Length of living room from sheathing line to partition center.
    F. Net width of kitchen between wall surfaces.
    G. Material used for finished floor in utility room.
    H. Cross-sectional size of ceiling joists.
    I. Spacing specified for ceiling joists.
    J. Size of access door to attic.
    K. Type of door shown between kitchen and hall.
    L. Type of window above kitchen sink.
    M. Outside width of plant box.
    N. Number of bathtubs.
    O. Thickness of rear stoop concrete slab.
    P. Type of finished floor in bedrooms.

2. A. _____
  B. _____
  C. _____
  D. _____
  E. _____
  F. _____
  G. _____
  H. _____
  I. _____
  J. _____
  K. _____
  L. _____
  M. _____
  N. _____
  O. _____
  P. _____

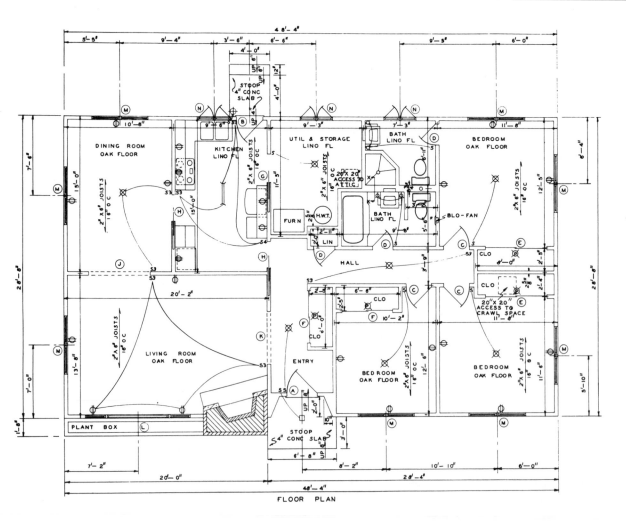

FLOOR PLAN

Name _____

3. The architect often uses symbols to indicate certain materials. Identify the basic materials represented by the symbols shown below.

3. A. _____

B. _____

C. _____

D. _____

E. _____

F. _____

G. _____

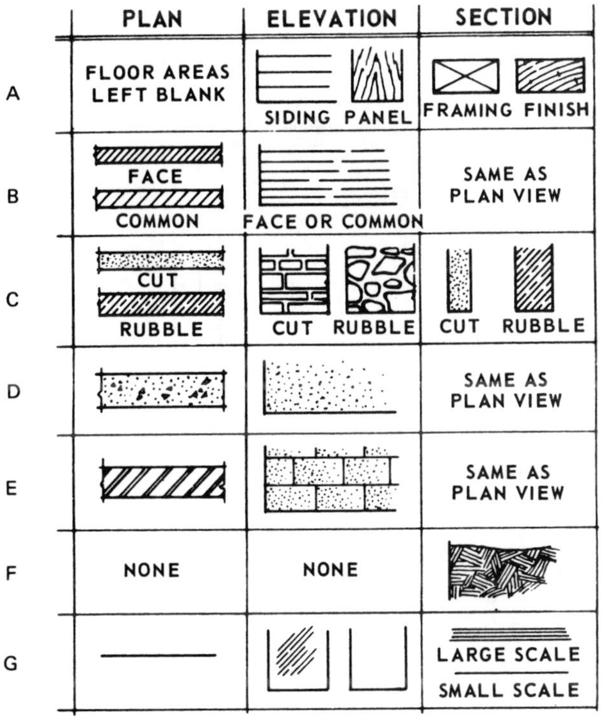

	PLAN	ELEVATION	SECTION
A	FLOOR AREAS LEFT BLANK	SIDING PANEL	FRAMING FINISH
B	FACE / COMMON	FACE OR COMMON	SAME AS PLAN VIEW
C	CUT / RUBBLE	CUT RUBBLE	CUT RUBBLE
D			SAME AS PLAN VIEW
E			SAME AS PLAN VIEW
F	NONE	NONE	
G	——		LARGE SCALE / SMALL SCALE

4. For most measurements over 2′ or 3′ long, the carpenter prefers to work with feet and inches. Find the total of the following measurements; 7′-4″, 3′-6″, 10′-10″, 12′-5″, 9′-10″, and then subtract 69″. (Make your calculations in the space below.)

4. _____

5. Below are several drawings representing different types of windows, doors, and other openings as seen in plan views. Identify each one.

OUTSIDE WALL

A

B

C

PARTITION

D

E

F

G

H

5. A. _____

B. _____

C. _____

D. _____

E. _____

F. _____

G. _____

H. _____

6. Simplified drawings and symbols are used to show plumbing fixtures, appliances, and mechanical equipment. Identify the following as seen in plan views.

A

B

C

D

E

F

G

H

6. A. _____

B. _____

C. _____

D. _____

E. _____

F. _____

G. _____

H. _____

7. Under a heading in the written specifications covering painting and finishing work, which one of the following would *not* be appropriate.

    A. Surfaces to be included (interior and exterior).
    B. Specifications of materials to be used.
    C. Application methods and number of coats.
    D. Number of painters to be used on the job.
    E. Guarantee of quality and performance.
    F. Completion date.

7. _____

8. Building codes are based on standards developed by manufacturers, government agencies, professionals, tradespeople, and _____.

8. _____

9. Commercial standards are developed by the Commodity Standards Division of the U.S. Department of _(A)_. These standards are designated by the letters _(B)_, followed by a code number and the year of the last revision.

9. A. _____

B. _____

Name _____

10. To secure a building permit the contractor or _____ must file an application
along with drawings and specifications.   10. _____

11. When work gets underway at the building site, a special card (furnished by
the local building department) must be posted. As each stage of construction
is completed, the card is signed by the _____.   11. _____

    A. contractor
    B. owner
    C. inspector
    D. carpenter

12. Explain the meaning of the term "setback."   12. _____

UNIT 7

Footings and Foundations

Text Pages 143-178

Name _____

Date _____ Score _____

1. To protect the owner and builder, the assistance of a registered engineer or licensed surveyor should be secured when laying out or checking _____.

    1. _____

2. When a laserplane, builders' level, or transit is not available, a right angle can be established by measured distances. In the drawing below, provide the measurements commonly used in this method.

    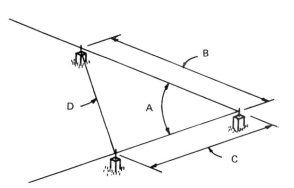

    2. A. _____

    B. _____

    C. _____

    D. _____

3. After building lines are established, it is good practice to check the length of _____ that exist in squares and rectangles to be sure that corners form a right angle.

    3. _____

4. A batter board assembly consists of stakes and one or more horizontal members. Each horizontal member is called a _____.

    A. bracket
    B. brace
    C. leveling strip
    D. ledger

    4. _____

5. For regular basement foundations in residential construction, the excavation should extend beyond the building lines by at least _____.

    A. 2′
    B. 3′
    C. 4′
    D. 5′

    5. _____

6. To protect wood framing, sheathing, and siding from moisture in the soil, it is generally recommended that foundations extend above the finished grade by _____.

    A. 6″
    B. 8″
    C. 10″
    D. 12″

6. _____

7. Load-bearing capacity of different type of soil vary considerably. A soil that consists of hard, dry clay, or coarse sand has a capacity of about _____ per sq. ft.

    A. 2000 lb.
    B. 4000 lb.
    C. 6000 lb.
    D. 8000 lb.

7. _____

8. Provide the recommended footing sizes in the drawing below. Consider the foundation wall to be 10″ thick.

8. A. _____

    B. _____

    C. _____

    D. _____

9. For a two-story residential structure it is recommended that chimney footings have a minimum thickness of __(A)__ and a minimum projection of __(B)__ on each side.

9. A. _____

    B. _____

10. A standard Number 5 reinforcing bar will have a diameter of _____.

    A. 1/4″
    B. 3/8″
    C. 1/2″
    D. 5/8″

10. _____

Name _____

11. The drawing below shows footing forms under construction. Identify the items specified.

11. A. _____

 B. _____

 C. _____

 D. _____

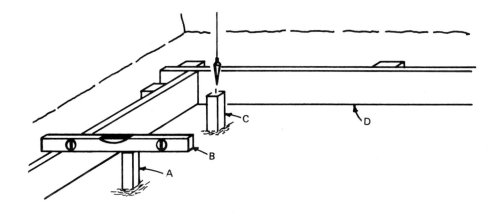

12. In preparing concrete, the cement and aggregate are mixed together and then water is added. The water causes a chemical action. This action is called _____.

12. _____

13. A standard sack of cement contains 1 cu. ft. and weighs _____.

13. _____

    A. 60 lb.
    B. 72 lb.
    C. 84 lb.
    D. 94 lb.

14. For general purpose work, concrete can be specified by listing the proportions of sand, cement, and gravel or crushed stone. Stone is seldom over _____ in diameter.

14. _____

    A. 1/2″
    B. 3/4″
    C. 1″
    D. 1 1/2″

15. A cubic yard of concrete will weigh about _____ lb. (Make your calculations in the space below.)

15. _____

16. Shown below is the lower section of a concrete wall form over 4′ high. Identify the various parts of the form as indicated.

16. A. _____

    B. _____

    C. _____

    D. _____

FOOTING

17. In regular residential construction, basement window openings are usually located so the weight of the overhead structure is carried by a _____.

17. _____

    A. precast lintel
    B. lintel blocks
    C. beam
    D. sill

18. The view below shows the installation of a(n) __(A)__. It is recommended that such an installation be made about every __(B)__ ′ along the foundation wall.

18. A. _____

    B. _____

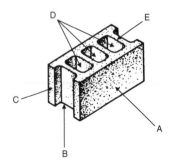

19. Name the parts of a concrete block indicated in the drawing below.

19. A. _____

    B. _____

    C. _____

    D. _____

    E. _____

Name _____

20. Standard concrete blocks are normally laid with a mortar joint that is _____ thick.

    A. 1/4″
    B. 3/8″
    C. 1/2″
    D. 5/8″

20. _____

21. Give the correct name for each type of concrete block shown below.

21. A. _____

    B. _____

    C. _____

    D. _____

    E. _____

    F. _____

    G. _____

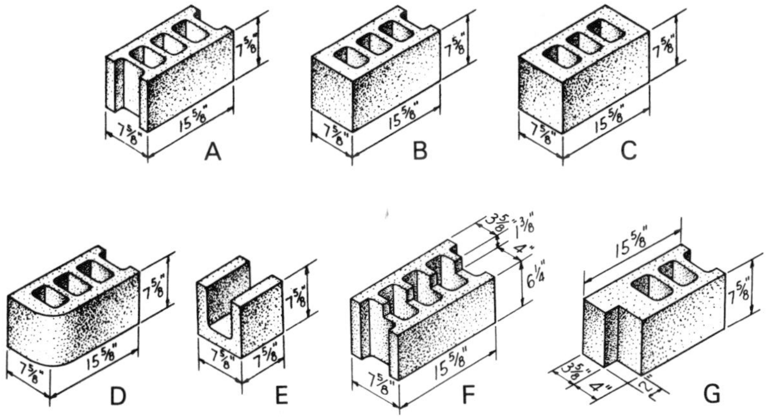

22. Complete the drawing below showing the footings, concrete block foundation wall, and basement floor. Provide adequate drainage and waterproofing for a very wet soil. Identify the various parts and applications.

22. _____

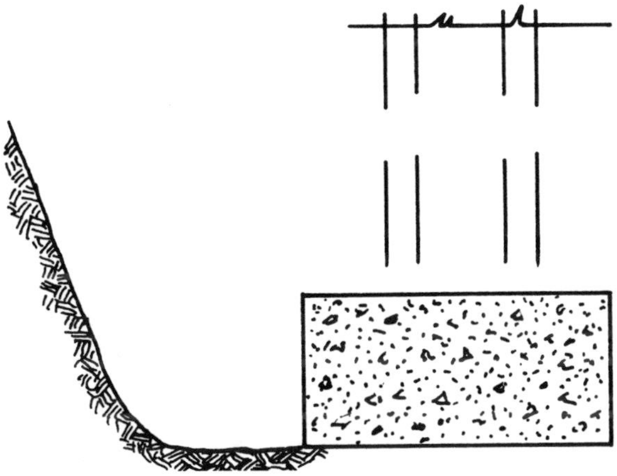

23. A masonry or steel structure is used to provide space around basement windows that are located below the finished grade. The name for this structure and space is _____.

23. _____

24. Slab-on-grade floors for residential structures should be insulated and protected against moisture. An approved detail is shown below. Identify the parts and materials.

24. A. _____

    B. _____

    C. _____

    D. _____

    E. _____

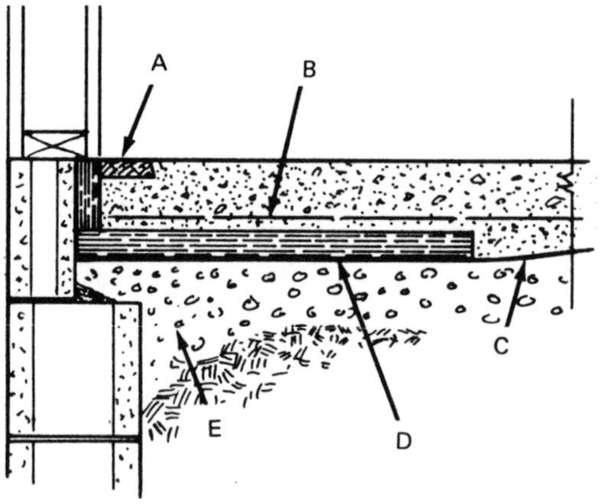

25. Expansion or control joints can be cut in concrete sidewalks or driveways with a power saw equipped with a masonry blade. For regular concrete, this operation should not be carried out until the concrete has cured for at least _____.

25. _____

    A. 18 hours
    B. 36 hours
    C. two days
    D. three days

26. An All-Weather Wood Foundation system is constructed from lumber that has been _____.

26. _____

    A. cut to oversized dimensions
    B. painted with a special green stain
    C. pressure treated with chemicals
    D. exposed to local weather conditions

27. To insure good drainage around a wooden foundation, a special basin for water collection is constructed. It is commonly referred to as a _____.

27. _____

    A. storm sewer
    B. drainage basin
    C. sump pit
    D. collector pit

28. It is important that inward forces against a wood foundation be transferred to the floor frame. Where joists run parallel to the wall, framing members called _____ should be installed between the outside joist and the first interior joist.

28. _____

Name _____

29. When placing (pouring) concrete, special protection should be provided
when temperatures fall below _____.   29. _____

    A. 0°F
    B. 20°F
    C. 32°F
    D. 40°F

30. Materials added to concrete or mortar to change its properties (freezing
point, curing time, etc.) are called _____.   30. _____

    A. inhibitors
    B. admixtures
    C. entraining agents
    D. accelerators

31. How many cubic yards of concrete will be needed to pour a basement floor
that measures 24′ × 54′ and is required to be 4″ thick? (Make your calculations in the space below.)   31. _____

32. How many cubic yards of concrete will be required to pour 216′ of footings
with a cross section of 8″ × 16″? Add 5% for waste and variation in forms
and round out your answer to the nearest 1/4 cu. yd. (Make your calculations
in the space below.)   32. _____

33. How many cubic yards of concrete will be needed to pour a foundation wall
10″ thick, 9′ high, and 20′ long? Do not figure any variation or waste and
round out your answer to the next higher 1/3 cu. yd. (Make your calculations
in the space below.)   33. _____

34. How many $8'' \times 8'' \times 16''$ concrete blocks will be required to lay a foundation wall with a total perimeter of 216' and specified to be 8' high? (Make your calculations in the space below.)

34. _____

35. One method of estimating the number of $8'' \times 8'' \times 16''$ concrete blocks needed for a wall is to divide the square footage of the face area by 100 and then multiply by _____.

35. _____

UNIT 8

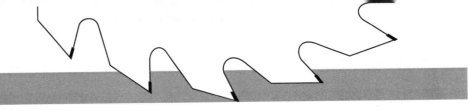

Floor Framing

Text Pages 179-207

Name _____

Date _____ Score _____

Unit 8 page 47

1. Installing the _____ _____ before backfilling helps the foundation withstand the pressure placed on it by the soil.

    1. _____
       _____

2. Identify the basic types of residential structures represented in the three drawings below.

    2. A. _____
       B. _____
       C. _____

A   B   C

3. Identify the structural members as specified in the drawings below.

    3. A. _____
       B. _____
       C. _____
       D. _____
       E. _____
       F. _____

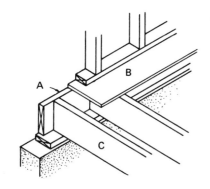
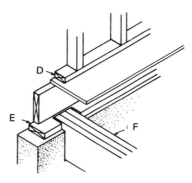

4. The two basic types of framing are platform and balloon. Platform framing is also referred to as _____ framing.

    4. _____

5. In balloon framing, the horizontal member that is attached to the studs and carries the second floor joists is called a _____.

    A. plate
    B. sill
    C. ribbon
    D. header

    5. _____

6. When calculating the size of girders and joists in residential construction, the first floor live load is usually specified as _____ lb. per sq. ft.

6. _____

    A. 20
    B. 30
    C. 40
    D. 50

7. The specified weight of a steel beam is based on the actual weight of a section _____ long.

7. _____

    A. 1″
    B. 12″
    C. 16″
    D. 100″

8. Provide the correct name for each of the parts specified in the drawings below.

8. A. _____
   B. _____
   C. _____
   D. _____
   E. _____
   F. _____

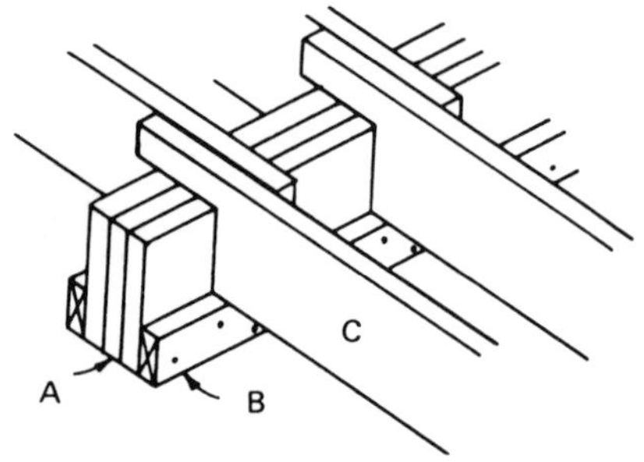

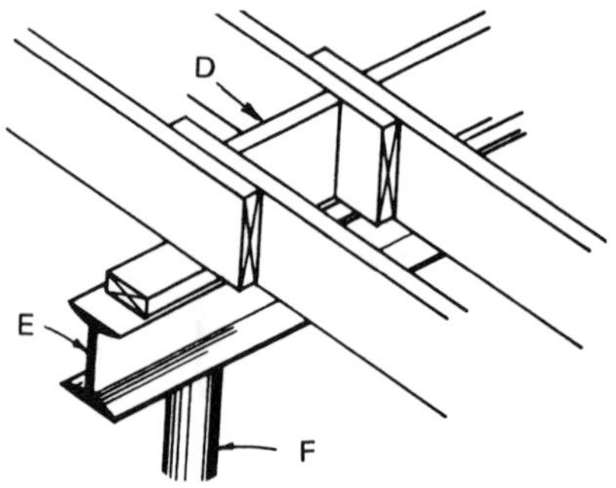

9. After girders or beams are set in place, the first step in building the floor frame is to _____.

9. _____

    A. lay out the position of the floor joist along the foundation wall
    B. lay out the joist spacing along the girders or beams
    C. attach sill to foundation walls
    D. cut joist headers to length and set them in place

10. Two types of steel beams are shown in the illustration below. Provide the correct size names for the S beam and part names as specified for the W beam.

10. A. _____
    B. _____
    C. _____
    D. _____

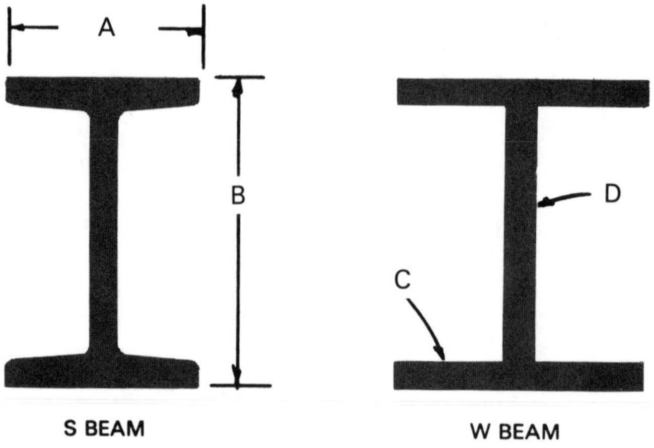

S BEAM   W BEAM

Name _____

11. Building codes usually specify that deflection (blending downward at the center) in a floor joist for residential buildings should not exceed 1/360 of the span under normal loads. What fraction of an inch would this equal for a span of 10′-0″? (Make your calculations in the space below.)

11. _____

12. Provide the correct distance in inches and fractions of an inch for the measurements identified in the drawing below.

12. A. _____

    B. _____

    C. _____

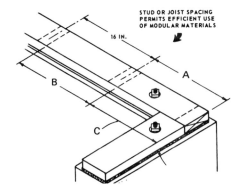

STUD OR JOIST SPACING
PERMITS EFFICIENT USE
OF MODULAR MATERIALS

16 IN.

13. Floor joists are attached to headers by nailing through the header and into the joists. The text suggests that the nailing pattern consist of _____ nails.

13. _____

    A. 2-20d
    B. 3-16d
    C. 3-20d
    D. 4-16d

14. The Uniform Building Code requires that, in standard framing, nails should not be spaced closer together than _____ of their total length.

14. _____

    A. one-eighth
    B. one-fourth
    C. one-half
    D. three-fourths

15. The drawing below shows the floor framing around an opening. Write the name for each of the specified parts.

15. A. _____

    B. _____

    C. _____

    D. _____

    E. _____

    F. _____

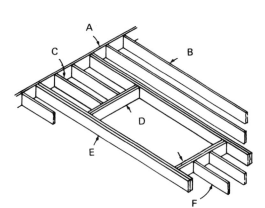

16. The National Forest Products Association recommends the use of metal framing anchors or ledger strips to support tail joists at an opening whenever they span a distance of _____ or more.

    A. 8'-0"
    B. 9'-0"
    C. 10'-0"
    D. 12'-0"

16. _____

17. Which of the following is *not* a purpose of bridging?

    A. Make each joist stronger.
    B. Hold joists in a vertical position.
    C. Transfer load from one joist to adjacent ones.

17. _____

18. Calculate the recommended measurements for the cantilevered joist shown in the drawing below. (Make your calculations in the space below.)

18. A. _____

    B. _____

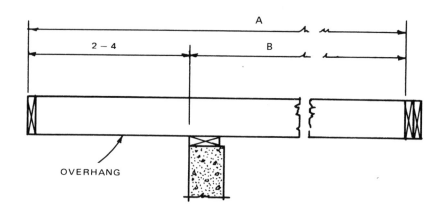

Name _____

19. When certain areas of a floor frame must support extra weight (bathroom fixtures, supporting partitions, or mechanical equipment), the joists should be spaced closer together and/or _____.

19. _____

20. If large holes must be cut into the joist to accommodate plumbing lines, they should be positioned _____.

20. _____

    A. near the top edge
    B. approximately in the middle
    C. near the bottom edge

21. FHA minimum requirements state that when floor joists are spaced 16″ in O.C. plywood thickness must be at least _____.

21. _____

    A. 3/8″
    B. 1/2″
    C. 5/8″
    D. 3/4″

22. Structural tests have shown that when a plywood subfloor is glued to the joists (instead of nailed), the stiffness of the floor is increased by about _____.

22. _____

    A. 25%
    B. 30%
    C. 35%
    D. 40%

23. Complete the drawing of a floor frame and foundation below. Also include the bottom of the wall frame. Design the construction so the exterior side of the foundation wall will be about level with the subfloor. Identify the various parts (3 Points For Correct Answer).

SHEATHING

SUBFLOOR

FOUNDATION

GRADE

24. The drawing below shows the nailing pattern for 5/8″ plywood being applied to joists spaced 16″ O.C. Give the correct measurement for spacing at A and B.

24. A. _____

    B. _____

25. In fastening steel joists to other steel members, which of the following methods are approved?

25. _____

    A. Self-tapping screws.
    B. Welding.
    C. Ring shanked nails.
    D. All of the above.

26. List two important safety precautions that should be taken when handling and welding metal joists.

_____

_____

27. Make an accurate estimate of the number and length of joists and headers required to construct the floor frame for a single-story rectangular building 12′ wide and 32′ long. Use 2 × 8 lumber spaced 16″ in O.C. (Make your calculations in the space below.)

	Number	Size
27. Headers:	_____	_____
Joists:	_____	_____
Total board feet:	_____	

28. Estimate the amount of subflooring required for the floor frame described in Problem 27. Provide figures for both 8″ shiplap and 5/8 × 4 × 8 sheets of plywood. (Make your calculations in the space below.)

Shiplap

28. Board feet: _____

    No. of sq. ft.: _____

Plywood

    No. of pieces: _____

    No. of sq. ft.: _____

Name _____

29. Estimate the total lineal feet and board feet of 2 × 6 material required for the floor frame sill of the residential plan shown in Unit 6, page 33, of the workbook. Most of the dimensions you will need are shown on the foundation plan. Include the 2 × 6 wood pad for the steel beam. Round out a given length to the next higher even dimension. For example, the right end wall is 28′-8″. Round it out to 30′-0″. This particular run would probably be made with one 14′ piece and one 16′ piece. (Make your calculations in the space below.)

29. Total lineal ft.: _____

Total bd. ft.: _____

30. Determine the total number of 2 × 8 × 16′ pieces needed to construct the floor frame. The 16′ joists will result in excessive overlap at the center and could be trimmed. The trimmings might be used for solid bridging blocks above the steel beam. Three 16′ pieces will form the header along the back wall if the side wall joist (stringer joist) overlaps the ends. Add one extra piece to form the double header at the fireplace opening, and 9 pieces for doubled joist under partitions. (Make your calculations in the space below.)

30. Total pieces: _____

Total bd. ft.: _____

31. Estimate the lineal (running) feet of wood bridging (size 1 × 3) for two runs of a floor frame that measures 48′ long. Most carpenters determine this figure by simply multiplying the total length of each double row of cross-bridging by 3. (Make your calculations in the space below.)

31. Lineal ft.: _____

Total bd. ft.: _____

32. Determine the number of sheets of plywood needed to lay the subfloor of a building that measures 24′ wide and 64′ long. What will be the total square footage of these pieces? (Make your calculations in the space below.)

32. Number
   of pieces.: _____
   Total sq. ft.: _____

33. Explain what you would do to frame a section of flooring to receive a concrete base so that the finished floor would be the same level as adjacent floors.

_____

_____

This on-site view shows a wall section being raised into place, after being assembled on the floor. The next unit includes questions and problems on this exciting phase of building construction.

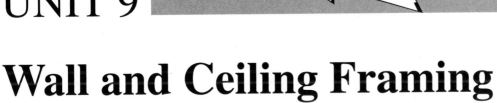

UNIT 9

Wall and Ceiling Framing

Text pages 205-232

Name _____

Date _____ Score _____

1. In platform construction, wall-framing members include sole plates, top plates, studs, headers, and _____.

    A. beams
    B. joists
    C. sheathing
    D. sills

1. _____

2. Although studs are sometimes spaced 24″ O.C. in residential structures, a spacing of _____ O.C. is more commonly used.

    A. 12″
    B. 16″
    C. 18″
    D. 20″

2. _____

3. Study the drawing of a typical wall frame shown below and identify the specified parts.

3. A. _____
    B. _____
    C. _____
    D. _____
    E. _____
    F. _____
    G. _____

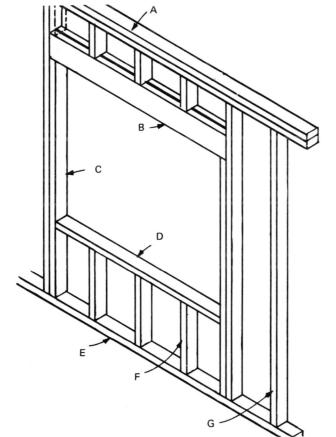

4. When assembling studs to form outside corners, it is recommended that
   _____ nails be used and that they be spaced 12″ apart.

   4. _____

   A. 8d
   B. 10d
   C. 12d
   D. 16d

5. The drawing below shows a plan view at the intersection of an outside wall
   and partition. Complete the drawing by sketching in the blocking and backing
   board commonly used to attach the two units.

OUTSIDE WALL

PARTITION

6. If the architectural plans show the rough opening of a window to be 3′-2″ ×
   4′-9″, the height of the opening should actually measure _____.

   6. _____

   A. 3′-3″
   B. 3′-2″
   C. 4′-9″
   D. 4′-11″

7. Headers are formed by nailing two members together with a spacer between.
   The spacer should be _____ thick.

   7. _____

   A. 1/4″
   B. 3/8″
   C. 1/2″
   D. 5/8″

8. When the R.O. in an outside wall is from 8′-0″ to 10′-0″ wide, the header
   should normally be constructed from _____ material.

   8. _____

   A. 2 × 6
   B. 2 × 8
   C. 2 × 10
   D. 2 × 12

9. When laying out the sole and top plate for an outside wall section, which of
   the following steps is *incorrect*?

   9. _____

   A. Lay out all centerlines of door and window openings.
   B. Lay out centerlines of intersecting partitions.
   C. Lay out all regular stud spacing and mark them with an X.
   D. Lay out two stud positions at each side of all openings.

Name _____

10. A master story pole provides full size measurements between floor levels, window, and door R.O. heights, thickness of various materials, and _____ _____.

10. _____

11. The first step in developing a master stud pattern is to lay out the _____.

11. _____

    A. position of headers
    B. position of sole plate
    C. distance from rough floor to ceiling

12. When making a master stud pattern lay out, the R.O. height of windows is measured from the _____.

12. _____

    A. top of header to the top of rough sill
    B. top of header to the bottom of rough sill
    C. bottom of header to the top of rough sill
    D. bottom of header to the bottom of rough sill

13. The drawing below shows a section of a wall frame. Provide the correct size of nail normally used at each identified point.

13. A. _____
    B. _____
    C. _____
    D. _____

14. When erecting wall sections, the carpenter can make sure they are exactly vertical by using either a level and straightedge or a _____ _____.

14. _____

15. In modern construction, studs are usually cut to exact length at the mill. They are designated by the letters _____.

15. _____

    A. P.E.T.
    B. E.P.T.
    C. T.E.L.
    D. C.T.L.

16. Boards and blocks installed in the wall framing for the sole purpose of mounting plumbing fixtures, towel bars, and other fixtures are called _____.

16. _____

17. When let-in wood bracing is required in a wall frame it is usually made from
    a _____.   17. _____

    A. 1 × 2
    B. 1 × 4
    C. 2 × 2
    D. 1 × 6

18. When installing the upper half of a double plate, use 10d nails and stagger
    the pattern with a spacing of _____.   18. _____

    A. 12″
    B. 16″
    C. 20″
    D. 24″

19. Complete the drawings below showing the correct installation of a double plate at corners and intersections.
    (2 Points for Correct Answer).

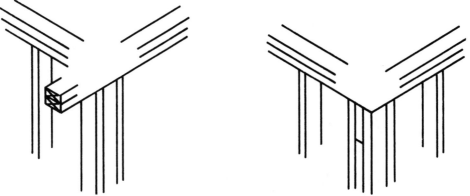

20. Standard thicknesses of fiberboard sheathing are 1/2″ and __(A)__. The 1/2″
    thickness is attached to the wall frame with roofing nails that are __(B)__ long.   20. A. _____
                                                                                             B. _____

Name _____

21. The drawing below shows the installation of metal strap bracing for 2×4 stud
framing. The strap is usually __(A)__ wide and attached with two __(B)__ nails.

21. A. _____

 B. _____

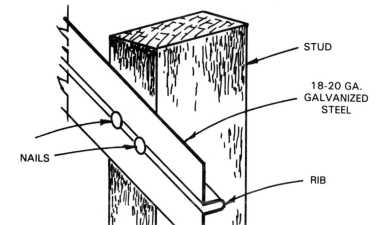

STUD

18-20 GA.
GALVANIZED
STEEL

NAILS

RIB

22. Rigid polystyrene foam sheathing that is 1″ thick will have an R value of
about _____.

 22. _____

    A. R-3
    B. R-4
    C. R-5
    D. R-7

23. The ceiling of a one-story building is supported by a framework made up of
members called _____ _____.

 23. _____

24. Partitions that run parallel to the members of the ceiling frame must be secured with blocking. Backing for
nailing ceiling surface material must also be included. Complete the drawing below showing how this is normally accomplished and identify the parts. (3 Points For Correct Answer)

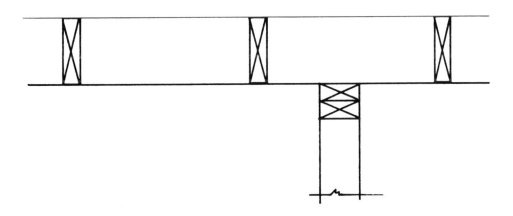

25. Look at the following illustration. Study the framing of the opening in the partition. Indicate under what conditions an interior partition can be framed as shown.

_____

_____

26. The following illustration shows a detail of a stud/ceiling joist assembly for steel framing. Identify the specified sections.

26. A. _____

    B. _____

    C. _____

    D. _____

    E. _____

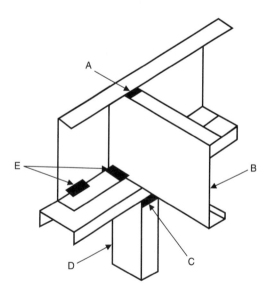

Name  _____

27. Look at the framing detail below and name the type of framing and the component being built.

27. _____

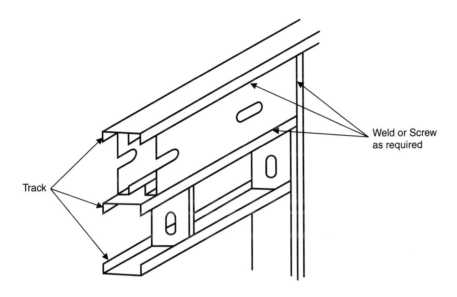

Weld or Screw
as required

Track

28. After adding up the length of all walls and partitions a carpenter finds there is a total of 270′. How many lineal feet of 2 × 4 stock will be needed to build the sole and double plate? How many bd. ft. will this equal? (Make your calculations in the space below.)

28. Lineal ft.: _____

Bd. ft.: _____

29. How many studs will be required for the wall framing described in the previous problem? Assume that the studs are spaced 16″ in O.C. and that there are 14 corners, 13 intersections, and 24 openings. Use the first (and longer) method described in the text. (Make your calculations in the space below.)

29. Total number
of studs: _____

30. After calculating the total exterior wall surface and subtracting for the major openings, it was found that the net area to be sheathed was 1220 sq. ft. How many pieces of 4 × 8 sheathing will be required if no allowance is made for waste? (Make your calculations in the space below.)

30. Total pieces: _____

UNIT 10

Roof Framing

Text Pages 233-271

Name _____

Date _____ Score _____

1. Five basic types of roof designs are shown in the illustration below. Identify each type.

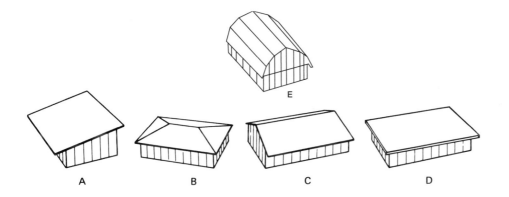

1.A. _____

B. _____

C. _____

D. _____

E. _____

2. A traditional roof design, similar to the hip roof except that the sides have a double slope, is called a _____ roof.

2. _____

3. The kind of rafters used to frame a hip roof constructed on a simple rectangular building include which three of the following types?

    common   hip jack
    cripple jack   valley
    hip   valley jack

3. _____

   _____

   _____

4. Identify the specified parts of the common rafter shown below.

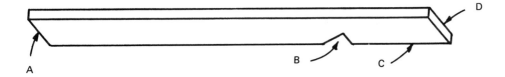

4. A. _____

B. _____

C. _____

D. _____

5. Basic terms and dimensions used in roof framing are shown in the drawing below. Identify each specified item.

5. A. _____

B. _____

C. _____

D. _____

E. _____

LINE FROM OUTSIDE
EDGE OF PLATE TO
CENTER LINE OF RIDGE

6. The slope of a roof is sometimes expressed as a fraction formed by placing the _____ over the _____.

pitch   run
rafter length   slope
rise   span

6. A. Numerator: _____

B. Denominator: _____

7. The blade of a standard framing square is _____ inches long.

7. _____

8. The side of a framing square that shows the manufacturer's name is called the _____.

8. _____

9. On the outside edge of the back of the framing square, the smallest division of an inch showing is _____.

A. 1/16″
B. 1/8″
C. 1/6″
D. 1/12″

9. _____

10. When laying out a common rafter using the step-off method, the second step in the procedure consists of _____.

A. shortening the rafter at the ridge
B. laying out the bird's mouth
C. laying out full units
D. laying out odd units

10. _____

11. In a given roof structure with a slope of 4 to 12, the run is specified as 8′-6″. Find the *line length* of a common rafter. The table number on the framing square is 12.65. Round out your answer to the nearest 1/8″. (Make your calculations in space below.)

11. _____

Name _____

12. To use a super square, the carpenter must know the roof _____.   12. _____

13. Manufacturers of super squares supply _____ _____ that enable the carpenter to determine the length of the rafter and the angle of the plumb cut.   13. _____

14. The illustration below shows a super square set to make a plumb cut on a common rafter. From the illustration, give the amount of rise per foot of run.   14. _____

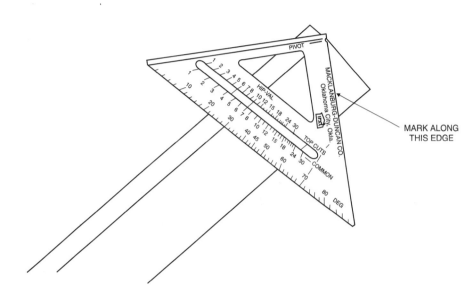

15. Show an approved nailing pattern (use 1/32″ dots) for attaching the rafters and ceiling joists to the double plate. Also specify nail sizes and indicate toenailing.

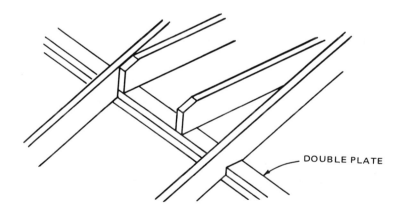

16. Which of the following items *would not* be used to calculate the length of the ridge for a hip roof constructed on a simple rectangular building?   16. _____

    A. Roof slope.
    B. Roof run.
    C. Length of building.
    D. Thickness of rafter stock.

17. When laying out a hip rafter, the same procedure is used as for the common rafter. An important difference, however, is that _____ is used on the blade of the framing square instead of 12″.

    A. 14″
    B. 16″
    C. 17″
    D. 20″

17. _____

18. Find the line length for a hip rafter when the slope of the roof is 4 to 12 and the run is 10'-2". The framing square table number is 17.44. Round out to the nearest 1/4″. (Make your calculations in the space below.)

18. Line length
    of hip rafter _____

19. A gable end frame that extends outward over brick veneer can be formed by using lookouts and blocking attached to a _____.

    A. sill
    B. ledger
    C. joist
    D. rafter

19. _____

20. The drawing below shows framing for an intersecting hip roof before jack rafters are installed. The framing members shown include ridges, common rafters, _(A)_ and one _(B)_.

20. A. _____

    B. _____

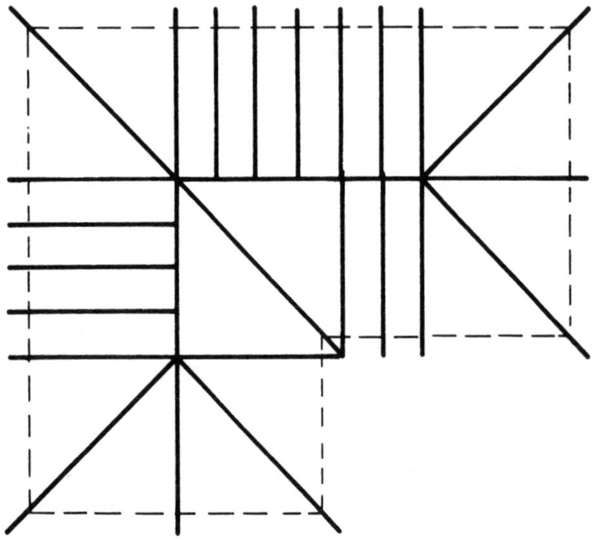

Name _____

21. Hip and valley rafters must be shortened at the ridge by a horizontal distance
equal to _____.

    21. _____

    A. one-half ridge thickness
    B. one-half of 45° thickness of rafter
    C. one-half of 45° thickness of ridge
    D. one-half of rafter thickness

22. The common difference in length of a set of jack rafters can be determined
by using the framing square as shown in the drawing below. Identify the
name of the points and distances specified.

    22. A. _____

         B. _____

         C. _____

23. The layout of the bird's mouth and overhang for a hip jack rafter is made or
secured from the _____.

    23. _____

    A. common rafter pattern
    B. hip rafter pattern
    C. framing square using common difference
    D. framing square table

24. Rafter tables can be used to lay out the side cut of jack rafters. Figures are
secured for the _____ line from the top.

    24. _____

    A. third
    B. fourth
    C. fifth
    D. sixth

25. Hip-valley cripple jack rafters located in a given roof section will be _____
(equal, unequal) in length.

    25. _____

26. When framing an opening for a chimney, a minimum clearance of _____
should be provided on each side and end.

    26. _____

27. A framed structure projecting above a sloping roof and which usually
includes a vertical window unit, is called a _____.

    27. _____

28. The drawing below shows horizontal framing members running between rafters on opposite sides of the roof frame. They provide a bracing effect and are called _____.

28. _____

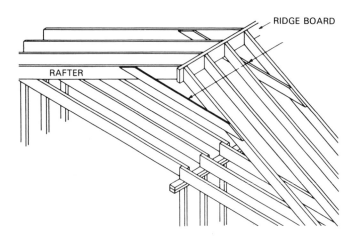

29. In flat roof framing, the main supporting members are called _____.

29. _____

30. A standard W or Fink truss is shown in the drawing below. Identify the specified members.

30. A. _____

B. _____

C. _____

D. _____

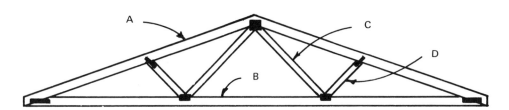

31. A standard roof truss with a length of 20′ or 30′ will usually require about _____ of camber.

31. _____

   A. 1/4″
   B. 3/8″
   C. 1/2″
   D. 3/4″

32. Two special truss designs are shown below. Provide the correct name for each.

32. A. _____

B. _____

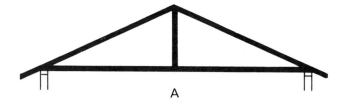

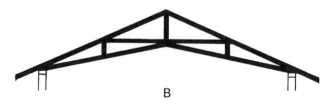

Name _____

33. The illustration below shows special gable end framing. Name the parts and indicate when such framing might be used.

_____

_____

_____

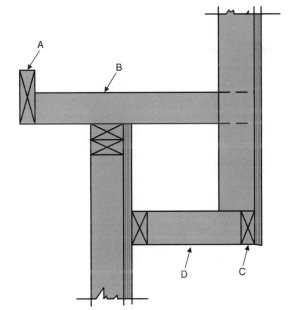

33. A. _____

 B. _____

 C. _____

 D. _____

34. Sheathing provides added strength and rigidity to the roof frame and also serves as a _____ _____ for the roof covering materials.

34. _____

35. At chimney openings, sheathing should be applied with a minimum clearance of _____ from the masonry.

35. _____

    A. 1/2″
    B. 1″
    C. 1 1/.2″
    D. 2″

36. The view below shows plywood sheathing being applied to rafters. What clearance should be maintained around chimney openings if sheathing board is used?

36. _____

    A. 5/16″
    B. 3/8″
    C. 1/2″
    D. 5/8″

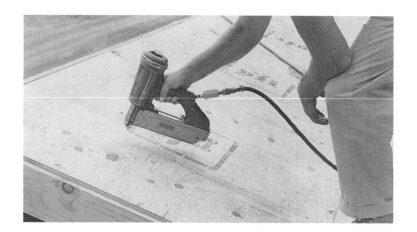

37. How many rafters will be required for a plain gable roof constructed on a rectangular building measuring 24′ × 48′? Slope of the roof is 5 to 12 and the specified rafter spacing is 16″ O.C. (Make your calculations in the space below.)

37. _____

38. Determine the number of standard length of 2 x 6 rafter stock needed to frame a *gable roof* on a rectangular building 24′ × 42′. The slope of the roof is 4 to 12 with a 1′ overhang. The rafter spacing is specified as 24″ O.C. Refer to the Technical Information section of the text to secure the rafter length. (Make your calculations in the space below.)

38. A. Length of rafter
      stock: _____

    B. Number of
      rafters: _____

    C. Total board
      feet: _____

Name _____

39. Estimate the number of pieces of standard length rafter stock needed to frame a hip roof on the building described in Problem 38. Use the 12″ scale on the framing square to determine the length of the hip rafters. (Make your calculations in the space below.)

    39. A. Total pieces of 14′ rafter stock: _____

          B. Length of stock needed for hip rafters: _____

40. How many pieces of 4 × 8 plywood will be required to sheath a plain gable roof on a building 26′ × 54′? The roof has a 2′ overhang, a slope of 3 to 12, and the rake extends over the gable end 6″. (Make your calculations in the space below.)

    40. A. No. of pieces: _____

          B. Total sq. ft.: _____

41. How many pieces of 4 × 8 plywood will be required to sheath a flat roof on a rectangular building 30′ × 66′? The roof overhang is 2′-6″ on all sides. (Make your calculations in the space below. Sometimes it is helpful to make a simple sketch.)

    41. A. No. of pieces: _____

          B. Total sq. ft.: _____

42. The total ground area for a plain structure with a gable (slope 4 to 12) is 1200 sq. ft. The roof overhang on sides and ends totals 220 sq. ft. Estimate the number of squares of roof surface. (Use table on page 313 of text.) Add 10% for waste and round your answer to the next higher full square. (Make your calculations in the space provided.)

    42. Squares: _____

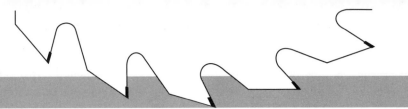

UNIT 11

Roofing Materials

Text Pages 275-316

Name _____

Date _____ Score _____

1. The materials applied to a sloping roof can contribute to the attractiveness of a building by adding texture, pattern, and _____.

1. _____

2. A trim board is normally applied to the lower edge of a sloping roof before the application of the surface material. The correct name of this member is _____.

2. _____

3. Roofing materials are estimated and sold by the _____. This is the amount of material needed to provide 100 sq. ft. of finished roof surface.

3. _____

4. Important distances used in the application of roofing materials are shown below. Provide the correct terms as specified.

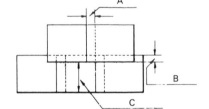

4. A. _____
   B. _____
   C. _____

5. The drawing below shows the application of underlayment and metal drip edge. Identify these two materials and the minimum lap distance specified.

5. A. _____
   B. _____
   C. _____
   D. _____

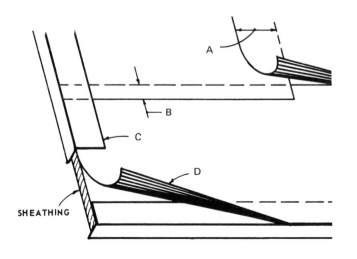

SHEATHING

6. An ice and water barrier, recommended for cold climates is laid down at the eaves and should extend _____ inside the wall line to prevent leak-through from ice dams and wind blown rain.

6. _____

    A. 1′
    B. 2′
    C. 3′
    D. 6′

7. Open valley flashing for asphalt shingles often consists of two strips of 90 lb. mineral surfaced asphalt roll roofing. The first strip should be not less than _____ wide. It is recommended that the second strip be at least _____ wide. When it is necessary to join either strip, they should be lapped at least _____. (Correct answers for all three blanks are included below.)

7. A. _____

    B. _____

    C. _____

| 8″ | 12″ | 16″ | 18″ | 20″ |
| 24″ | 28″ | 30″ | 36″ | 40″ |

8. Shingles are laid along the sides of an open valley so that a 6″ wide water-way starts at the ridge and increases in width _____ inch(es) per foot as they approach the eave. What would be the width at the eave for a valley 11′ long? (Make your calculations in the space below.)

8. _____

_____

9. _____

9. Metal flashing shingles are commonly used to waterproof joints between sloping roofs and vertical walls. This type of flashing is usually called _____.

    A. step-flashing
    B. wall-flashing
    C. cap-flashing
    D. corner-flashing

10. Nails used to apply asphalt shingles should have a large head and weather-proof characteristics. Provide the correct name for the three types shown below.

10. A. _____

    B. _____

    C. _____

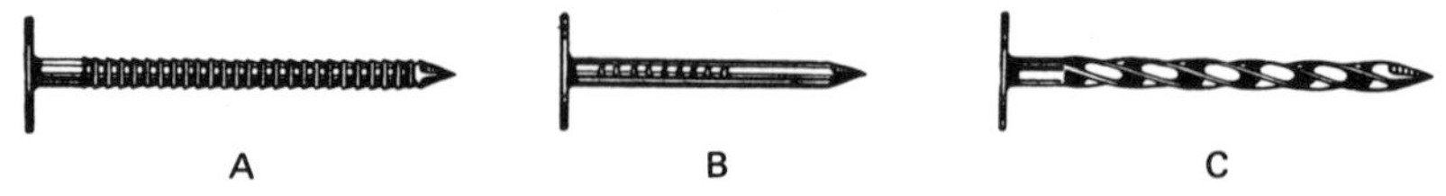

A   B   C

Name _____

11. Staple guns are becoming more popular on shingling jobs. Length of staples recommended depends on the thickness of the deck. Give appropriate staple lengths for the following deck thicknesses.

    A. 3/8″
    B. 1/2″
    C. 5/8″
    D. 3/4″

11. A. _____

    B. _____

    C. _____

    D. _____

12. A standard three-tab strip shingle is shown in the drawing below. Provide the correct sizes as specified by the dimension lines.

12. A. _____

    B. _____

    C. _____

SELF-SEALING ADHESIVE

13. Three-tab square-butt shingles are commonly laid so the cutouts are centered over the tab in the course directly below. The first course is started with a full strip and the second course is started with _____.

    A. a strip from which one tab has been removed
    B. a strip from which one-half tab has been cut away
    C. one-half of a shingle tab

13. _____

14. Flashing around a masonry chimney consists of two parts: base flashing which is attached to the roof and _____ or counter flashing that is attached to the chimney.

14. _____

15. The drawing below shows the applications of hip and ridge shingles with a 5″ exposure. Provide the nailing distances specified.

15. A. _____

    B. _____

5 IN. EXPOSURE

16. For low-sloped roofs, a double underlayment is cemented together to form eave flashing. This flashing should be carried up the roof to a point at least _____ inside the interior wall line.

    A. 18″
    B. 24″
    C. 36″
    D. 48″

16. _____

17. Double coverage roll roofing can be used on slopes as low as _____ per foot.   17. _____

    A. 1"
    B. 1 1/2"
    C. 2"
    D. 2 1/2"

18. Double coverage roll roofing consists of a granular surfaced area and a smooth area. The smooth area is called a selvage and is _____ wide.   18. _____

    A. 18"
    B. 19"
    C. 20"
    D. 21"

19. The nails used in the application of asphalt shingles over old wood shingles must be long enough to penetrate well into the sheathing. This usually requires nails that are _____ long.   19. _____

    A. 1 1/4"
    B. 1 3/8"
    C. 1 1/2"
    D. 1 3/4"

20. The drawing below shows the parts and installation of a flat roof overhang. Identify the specified items.

20. A. _____

    B. _____

    C. _____

    D. _____

    E. _____

Name _____

21. Basic construction at the intersection of a flat roof and wall is shown below. Identify the parts and minimum distance as specified.

21. A. _____
    B. _____
    C. _____

22. Wood shingles are produced in random widths and lengths of 16″, 18″, and _____ inches. They are packaged in bundles. For a standard application, one bundle will cover about _____.

22. A. _____
    B. _____

23. When using wood shingles on low sloped (less than 5 to 12) roofs, the exposure should be reduced to a point that will provide no less than _____ layers of shingles at any given point.

23. _____

    A. 2
    B. 3
    C. 4
    D. 5

24. The drawing below shows wood shingles being applied according to standard specifications. Note that each shingle is secured with two nails. Provide the recommended spacing and distances as specified.

24. A. _____

    B. _____

    C. _____

    D. _____

25. Wood shakes are highly durable but they must be applied to roofs that have sufficient slope to insure good drainage. The recommended minimum slope is _____.

25. _____

    A. 4 to 12
    B. 5 to 12
    C. 5 1/2 to 12
    D. 6 to 12

26. Three types of wood shakes are generally available as shown in the drawing below. Identify each type.

26. A. _____

    B. _____

    C. _____

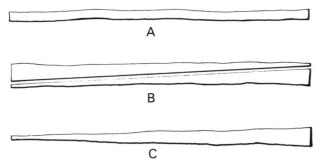

A

B

C

27. After each course of wood shakes is nailed into place an 18″ strip of _____ is applied over the upper portion of the shakes and extended onto the sheathing.

27. _____

28. Tile roofing, made from concrete or fired clay, weighs from _(A)_ to _(B)_ lb./sq. ft.

28. A. _____

    B. _____

29. Strips of wood called _____ are fastened horizontally to the roof deck to hold tile roofing in place. They are spaced _____ inches apart; _____ molded to the underside of the tiles hook onto the battens.

29. A. _____

    B. _____

    C. _____

Name _____

30. In the application of corrugated sheet metal roofing it is recommended that side laps be made to include _____ corrugations.

    A. 1
    B. 1 1/4
    C. 1 1/2
    D. 2

30. _____

31. Terne metal roofing is made from copper-bearing steel sheets that have been hot dipped in an alloy of _____.

    A. lead and tin
    B. tin and zinc
    C. lead and copper
    D. copper and zinc

31. _____

32. Shown below are several components used in a gutter system. Give the general name of each item.

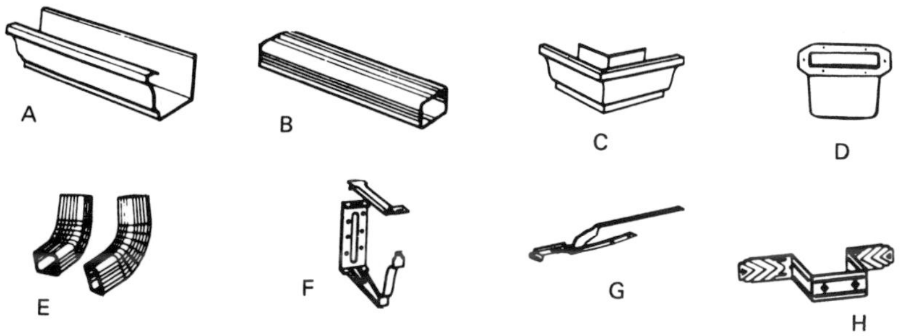

32. A. _____
     B. _____
     C. _____
     D. _____
     E. _____
     F. _____
     G. _____
     H. _____

33. The total ground area plus overhang of a house with a gable roof (slope 5 to 12) is 1880 sq. ft. Figure 10% for waste and calculate the number of squares of asphalt shingles required. Round out your answer to the nearest full square. (Make your calculations in the space below.)

33. Squares: _____

34. A rectangular building with a plain gable roof has a common rafter length of 14′. The total length of the ridge is 30′. Calculate the number of full bundles of wood shingles required. Add 10% for waste. (Make your calculations in the space below.)

34. Bundles: _____

35. A 28 × 48 building has a hip roof (slope 6 to 12) with a 2′ overhang. How many full bundles of wood shingles will be required? Figure 10% waste and then add one additional square for the hips. (Make your calculations in the space below.)

    35. Bundles: _____

36. Estimate the number of squares of asphalt shingles required for a large storage building, 20′ × 80′. The shed type roof (slope 4 to 12) has a 3′ overhang on the upper edge. Use the table on page 313 of the textbook and add 10% for waste. Round out your answer to the nearest full square. (Make your calculations in the space below.)

    36. Squares: _____

37. A folding carpenter's rule is being used to determine the pitch of a roof. The "reading point" on the rule is at 20 1/2. Refer to Figure 11-79 and indicate the pitch and slope of the roof.

    37. Pitch: _____

    Slope: _____

UNIT 12

Windows and Exterior Doors

Text Pages 317 -350

Name _____

Date _____ Score _____

1. Woodworking factories that produce windows and doors are commonly called _____ plants.

1. _____

2. Quality control in the manufacture of windows is based on guidelines established by U.S. Commercial Standards and the _____ Association.

    A. Architectural Woodwork
    B. Western Wood Products
    C. National Woodwork Manufacturers
    D. National Forest Products

2. _____

3. A window that consists of two sashes that slide up and down in the frame is called _____.

3. _____

4. The view below shows a window installation consisting of casement units, both operating and fixed. Provide the correct terms of the various parts and sections as specified.

4. A. _____

    B. _____

    C. _____

    D. _____

    E. _____

5. Where it is desirable to insure privacy or provide wall space for furniture arrangements, a "ribbon" of short window units is sometimes installed high on the wall. _____ windows are especially adaptable to such an installation.

5. _____

6. In residential construction the standard height of windows, measured from the bottom side of the head to the finished floor is _____.

    A. 6'-6"
    B. 6'-8"
    C. 6'-10"
    D. 7'-0"

6. _____

7. Window glass is a major source of heat loss. A single layer of standard glass has an R-value of about 0.88. A double pane of the same glass with a 1/2" air space between has an R-value of about _____.

    A. 2.75
    B. 2.00
    C. 1.50
    D. 1.25

7. _____

8. Glass used in regular windows is produced by a process called _____.

    A. drawing
    B. stamping
    C. floating
    D. rolling

8. _____

9. Double and triple glazing improves insulating values and reduces noise transmission. For a standard movable sash, two or three layers of 1/8" glass are fused together with a _____ air space between each layer.

    A. 1/8"
    B. 3/16"
    C. 3/8"
    D. 1/2"

9. _____

10. Architectural drawings show the type of windows in the elevation views. The drawings below are standard representations of four types. Provide the correct name for each one.

10. A. _____

    B. _____

    C. _____

    D. _____

A

B

HINGE LINE

C

HINGE LINE

D

Name _____

11. Architectural drawings usually include a table (called a window schedule) that lists the manufacturer, unit size, and the rough opening (R.O.). If an R.O. for a given window was listed as 2'-10″ × 3'-4″, the actual height of the framed opening should be _____.

11. _____

    A. 2'-10″
    B. 3'-0″
    C. 3'-4″
    D. 3'-6″

12. The horizontal location of window units is shown on the floor plans. In masonry construction, this dimension is usually given to the _____ of the opening.

12. _____

    A. centerline
    B. edge
    C. middle

13. Basically, windows consist of glass panels mounted in a sash, and the sash is installed in a frame. Standard details of the constructions are usually included in three sectional views as shown below. Provide the correct name for each view.

13. A. _____

     B. _____

     C. _____

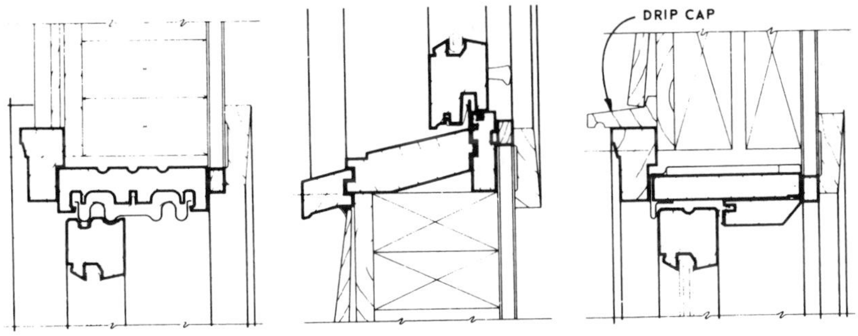

DRIP CAP

A   B   C

14. The illustration below shows a double-hung window located on each side of a fixed unit. The two sections where the units are joined together are called _____.

14. _____

15. The first step in installing a window is to check the rough opening. Most windows require at least 1/2″ clearance on each side and _____ above the head.

    A. 1/2″
    B. 3/4″
    C. 1″
    D. 1 1/2″

15. _____

16. Standard window units can be adjusted to walls of various thicknesses. This adjustment consists of attaching a special strip to the window edges. This strip is called a _____.

    A. sill spreader
    B. jamb extension
    C. jamb ribbon
    D. frame spacer

16. _____

17. After the window unit is placed in the rough opening and secured temporarily, the next step is to _____.

    A. check the corners with a framing square
    B. nail through the lower end of the side casing
    C. raise frame to correct height as marked on story pole
    D. set wedges under the sill and nail it in place

17. _____

18. Standard windows made with wooden frames are permanently secured by driving weatherproofed casing nails through the casing and into the building frame. The nails should be spaced _____.

    A. 12″ O.C.
    B. 16″ O.C.
    C. 18″ O.C.
    D. 20″ O.C.

18. _____

19. In modern construction, large fixed glass areas are usually fitted with sealed double glazing. Shown below are cross-sectional views of sash or frames with 3/4″ glass units in place. Identify the parts and materials, and provide recommended clearance as specified.

19. A. _____
    B. _____
    C. _____
    D. _____
    E. _____

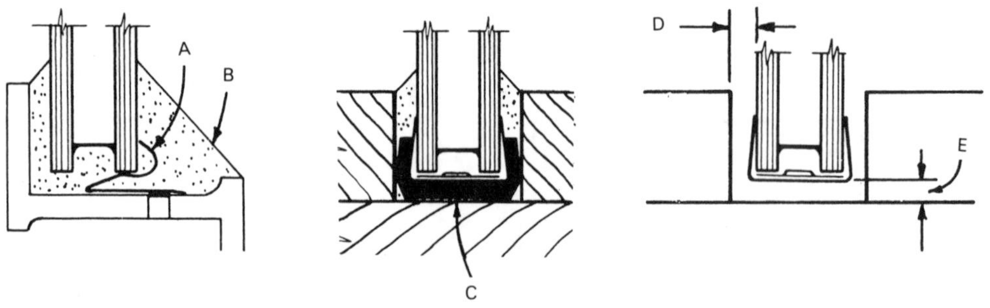

20. The actual sizes of glass blocks are somewhat smaller than the nominal sizes. The actual dimensions of a 12 × 12 unit are _____.

    A. 3 7/8 × 11 3/4 × 11 3/4
    B. 3 3/4 × 11 3/4 × 11 3/4
    C. 3 5/8 × 11 5/8 × 11 5/8
    D. 3 7/8 × 11 7/8 × 11 7/8

20. _____

Name _____

21. What size opening would be required for a glass block installation consisting of 6″ blocks that was 9 units wide and 11 units high? (Make your calculations in the space below.)

21. Width: _____

Height: _____

22. When replacing windows one of the first steps is to remove the inside trim. The next step is to _____.

22. _____

    A. pry off outside casing
    B. remove inside stops and lift out lower sash
    C. make saw cuts through sill
    D. remove parting stops and lift out upper sash

23. Skylights that consist of a hinged sash should not be installed in roofs with less than a _____ slope.

23. _____

    A. 5 to 12
    B. 4 to 12
    C. 3 to 12
    D. 2 to 12

24. An insulated shaft is used to connect a skylight with the room ceiling below. When this shaft is flared out on all four sides it is called a _____ shaft.

24. _____

    A. coffered
    B. truncated
    C. domed
    D. splayed

25. Exterior doors for residential construction are usually _____ high. FHA Minimum Property Standards list a minimum exterior door width of _____.

25. A. _____

B. _____

26. Exterior door frames are similar to window frames. Sectional views show details and sizes. Identify the detailed views shown below.

26. A. _____

B. _____

C. _____

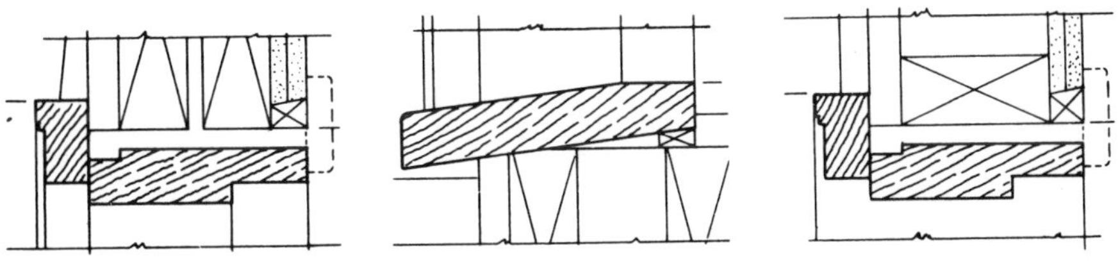

A   B   C

27. For standard residential construction, the R.O. of an exterior door can be calculated by adding _____ to the door width and height.

    A. 3/4″
    B. 1″
    C. 1 1/4″
    D. 2 1/2″

27. _____

28. When installing an exterior door frame, extra wedges or blocking should be located in the approximate position of the lock strike plate and the _____.

28. _____

29. Prehung exterior door units are fastened in place by driving _____ finishing nails through the jambs, shims, and into the structural frame members.

    A. 8d
    B. 10d
    C. 16d
    D. 20d

29. _____

30. The drawing below shows the lower sectional view of a two panel sliding glass door. Identify the parts as specified.

30. A. _____

    B. _____

    C. _____

    D. _____

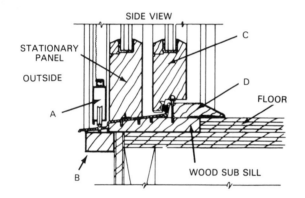

31. The view below shows the installation of a sliding glass door frame. Before nailing the sill into place it is generally recommended that _____.

    A. a layer of the subfloor be removed
    B. a bead of sealing compound be applied
    C. one door be set in place and checked
    D. one side jamb be plumbed and nailed

31. _____

Name _____

32. There are three basic types of garage doors: hinged or swinging, _____, and roll-up.

32. _____

33. Standard heights for modern residential garage doors include 6′-6″ and _____.

33. _____

    A. 6′-8″
    B. 6′-10″
    C. 7′-0″
    D. 7′-6″

34. To offset the weight of roll-up garage doors, an effective counter-balance is required. The two most commonly used in residential installations are the extension spring and the _____ spring. The latter is shown in the view below.

34. _____

35. Name the three components of a low-e window.

35. _____

    _____

    _____

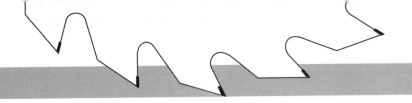

UNIT 13

Exterior Wall Finish

Text Pages 351-389

Name _____

Date _____ Score _____

1. In general, the term "exterior finish" includes the application of all exterior surfaces of a structure, including the roofing materials. It includes the construction of the cornice and rake, and the application of siding and trim members around __(A)__ and __(B)__.

1. A. _____

  B. _____

2. An open cornice is used when the style of architecture requires the _____ to be exposed to view.

2. _____

3. The drawing below shows the structural and trim members of a boxed cornice for a low-pitched roof. Identify the parts specified.

3. A. _____

  B. _____

  C. _____

  D. _____

  E. _____

  F. _____

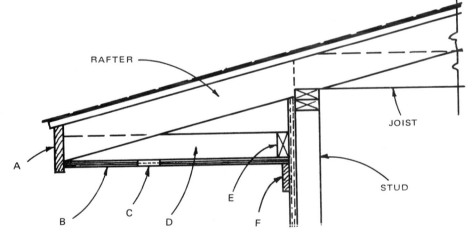

4. When plywood or other thin material is used for the soffit of a boxed cornice, the edge along the fascia should be supported. This can be accomplished with a groove cut in the fascia or by a _____ attached to the rafters and/or fascia.

4. _____

5. A closed or boxed cornice should have screened slots or patented ventilating units installed in the _____.

5. _____

6. The rake is the part of the roof that overhangs a gable. Shown below is a wide boxed rake section. Identify the trim members as specified.

6. A. _____

   B. _____

   C. _____

   D. _____

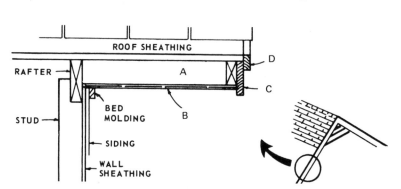

7. In a conventional boxed cornice with a sloping roof and a horizontal soffit, the ledger strip serves several functions. In the list below select the item that is of little or no importance.

7. _____

   A. Secures the inside end of the lookout to the wall frame.
   B. Secures sheathing to wall studs.
   C. Provides a nailing base for soffit material.
   D. Provides support, through the lookout, to the rafter tail.

8. The end views of various types of horizontal siding are shown in the drawing below. Identify each type.

8. A. _____

   B. _____

   C. _____

   D. _____

   E. _____

   F. _____

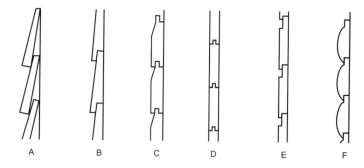

9. Aluminum and vinyl are two types of material used to finish cornices. In the cut-away drawing below, a vinyl soffit is being installed. Name the specified parts of the system.

9. A. _____

   B. _____

   C. _____

   D. _____

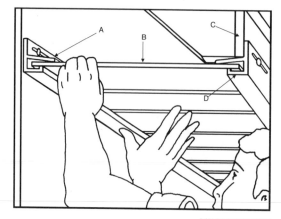

ROLLEX CORPORATION

Name _____

10. The recommended overlap of beveled siding is _____.   10. _____

    A. 7 1/4″
    B. 7 3/8″
    C. 7 1/2″
    D. 7 5/8″

11. When horizontal siding is applied over sheathing that consists of solid wood, plywood, or nail-base fiberboard, the nails can be spaced (horizontally) about _____ apart.   11. _____

    A. 12″
    B. 16″
    C. 20″
    D. 24″

12. In modern residential construction, new products have been developed to replace older types of sheathing and sheathing paper. Which of the following would be included in this group of new materials?   12. _____

    A. Asphalt-saturated felt with high moisture vapor resistance.
    B. Rigid polystyrene insulating board.
    C. Housewrap.
    D. Asphalt-saturated felt with low moister vapor resistance.

13. When windows or doors are not protected by a wide overhang, certain extra installations should be made. Identify the items specified in the drawing below.   13. A. _____

    B. _____

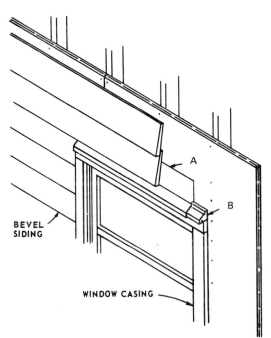

BEVEL SIDING

WINDOW CASING

14. Plain beveled siding is lapped so it will provide a tight exterior wall covering. In a standard installation, 10″ beveled siding is lapped about _____.

    A. 1″
    B. 1 1/2″
    C. 1 3/4″
    D. 2″

14. _____

15. The two views below show a carpenter using a _____ to lay out the position of siding courses at corners and openings.

15. _____

16. In modern residential construction, the ends of beveled siding are joined at outside corners with a _____.

16. _____

17. When wooden corner boards are used for a horizontal siding application, they are installed _____ (before, after) the siding is applied.

17. _____

18. In the application of wide (8″ or more) bevel siding, drive the nail through the siding slightly _____ (above, below) the top edge of the previously applied course.

18. _____

19. How many square feet of 1 × 8 bevel siding will be required to cover a wall 8′-0″ high and 30′-0″ long? The total window area is 30 sq. ft. Check the table on page 364 of the text and round out your answer to the nearest even number of square feet. (Make your calculations in the space below.)

19. sq. ft.: _____

20. Figure the amount of 1 × 10 bevel siding required to cover a rectangular building 24′ × 50′. The outside walls are 9′ high and the total rise of the gable roof is 4′. Total window and door area is 200 sq. ft. Add 10% to the area of the gable ends for waste. Check the table on page 364 of the text and round out your answer to the nearest even number of square feet. (Make your calculations in the space below.)

20. sq. ft.: _____

Name _____

21. Wood shingles are sometimes used for wall coverings. In a single-coursed application of 16″ shingles, the recommended maximum exposure is _____.   21. _____

    A. 4 1/2″
    B. 5 1/2″
    C. 6 1/2″
    D. 7 1/2″

22. The illustration below shows the application of battens over vertical siding consisting of solid boards. Battens are attached by nailing through _____.   22. _____

    A. the center
    B. along one edge
    C. along both edges

23. EIFS stands for Exterior _____ Finishing System   23. _____

24. EIFS wall coverings may only be installed over concrete or concrete block. True or False.   24. _____

25. Standard application requirements for vertical plywood siding panels states that edge nailing should be spaced _____.   25. _____

    A. 4″ O.C.
    B. 6″ O.C.
    C. 8″ O.C.
    D. 12″ O.C.

26. The view below shows a vinyl siding system being installed. Allowances must be made for expansion and contraction caused by _____.

    A. aging
    B. temperature
    C. moisture

26. _____

27. Hardboard sidings are available in a wide range of textures and surface treatments. The most common thickness is _____.

    A. 5/16″
    B. 3/8″
    C. 7/16″
    D. 1/2″

27. _____

28. Basic specifications for aluminum siding covering metal qualities and gage requirements are established by the FHA and _____.

28. _____

29. Aluminum siding should be grounded. Recommendations state that the siding application should be connected to the cold water service or the electrical service ground with a _____ or larger wire.

    A. No. 8
    B. No. 10
    C. No. 12
    D. No. 14

29. _____

30. Vinyl siding and accessories are produced by a process called _____.

    A. vacuum forming
    B. extrusion
    C. hot rolling
    D. roll forming

30. _____

Name _____

31. The base for stucco consists of sheathing, sheathing paper, and heavily galvanized metal lath. The lath should be spaced _____ away from the sheathing surface.

    31. _____

    A. 1/8″
    B. 1/4″
    C. 3/8″
    D. 7/16″

32. The drawing below shows brick veneer construction just above the foundation level. Identify the specified items.

    32. A. _____
        B. _____
        C. _____
        D. _____
        E. _____

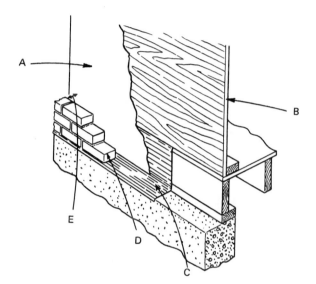

33. To ensure that water or moisture is not trapped behind brick veneer construction, small holes (called weep holes) are made in the joints of the lowest course of bricks. It is recommended that weep holes be spaced _____ apart.

    33. _____

    A. 16″
    B. 32″
    C. 40″
    D. 48″

34. The illustration below shows a home with shutters added to the window units. Note how they improve the appearance—especially the bedroom projection. Which one of the following statements is *incorrect* concerning modern shutters.

    34. _____

    A. Modern shutters are used mainly for decorative effects.
    B. Shutters are usually attached with special concealed hinges.
    C. Shutters are available in standard widths that range from 14″ to 20″
    D. Shutter installation should permit easy removal for painting and maintenance.

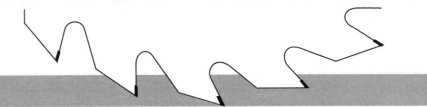

UNIT 14

Thermal and Sound Insulation

Text Pages 393-428

Name _____

Date _____ Score _____

1. In a normal sequence of residential construction, insulation materials are not installed until the rough-in of plumbing, _____, and electrical wiring has been completed.

1. _____

2. Heat is transferred through floors, walls, ceilings, windows, and doors at a rate that varies with the temperature (inside and outside) and the _____ to heat flow provided by the intervening materials.

2. _____

3. Heat moves from one molecule to another within a given material or from one material to another when they are in direct contact. This method of heat movement or transmission is called _____.

3. _____

4. The diagrams below show two methods commonly used to heat enclosed space. Provide the correct term used to identify these heat transmission methods.

4. A. _____

   B. _____

A

B — HEATER

5. A good insulation material must offer a high resistance to heat transmission. It also should be fireproof, vermin-proof, _____, and resistant to any physical change that will reduce its effectiveness.

5. _____

6. The coefficient of thermal conductivity (k) is the amount of heat transferred in one _(A)_ through one sq. ft. of a given material that is _(B)_ thick and has a temperature difference of 1°F between its surfaces.

6. A. _____

   B. _____

7. How many British thermal units of heat will be required to raise 16.5 lb. of water from 33°F to 97°F? (Make your calculations in the space below.)　　7. _____

8. A U-value is like a k-value except it may consist of several materials, thicknesses, and air spaces. Pictured below is a ceiling section. Select the correct U-value for the insulated area as indicated.　　8. _____

    A. U = 0.10
    B. U = 0.05
    C. U = 0.08
    D. U = 0.03

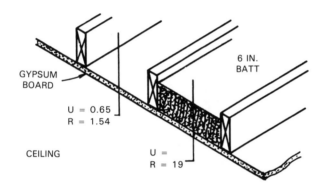

9. Shown below are two identical wall sections except for insulation. Select the correct R-value for the insulated wall as specified.　　9. _____

    A. R-10
    B. R-12
    C. R-14
    D. R-16

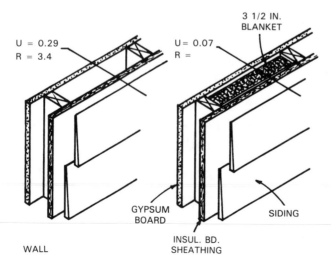

Name _____

10. A composite U-value cannot be secured by adding (k) and U-values of the various parts of a structure. However, R-values can be used. Calculate the U-value of a wall where the R-values can be used. Calculate the U-value of a wall where the R-values of sheathing, siding, air spaces, plaster, and insulation total 11.5. Round out your answer to the third decimal place. (Make your calculations in the space below.)

10. _____

11. A wall constructed of 2×6 studs is sheathed with 3/4″ insulation board, wrapped with Tyvek, and sided with 3/4″ wood bevel siding. Insulation consists of 5 1/2″ glass fiber batts over which has been installed 5/8″ gypsum board. The approximate R-value of the wall is _____. (Make your calculations in the space below.)

11. _____

12. A "degree day" is the product of one day and the number of degrees Fahrenheit the average temperature for that day is below _____°F. Figures are usually totaled for a full year and are helpful in determining insulation requirements.

12. _____

13. Insulation for conventional structures can be grouped into four broad classifications. They include loose fill, flexible, rigid, and _____.

13. _____

14. Three types of insulation commonly used in walls and ceilings of residential structures are shown below. Identify each one.

14. A. _____

B. _____

C. _____

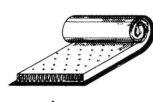

A

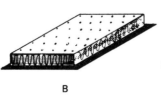

B

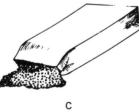

C

15. In modern construction, a rigid insulation board widely used in masonry walls and floors is made of _____.

    15.

    A. foamed glass
    B. cork board
    C. foamed plastic
    D. vermiculite

16. To be effective, reflective insulation must be exposed to an air space. The minimum recommended depth of this space is _____.

    16. _____

    A. 1/2″
    B. 3/4″
    C. 1″
    D. 1 1/2″

17. The view below shows the essential requirements for an unheated crawl space. Insulation is placed between the joists. The vapor barrier used to cover the ground should be 6-mil (.006″) polyethylene film or roll roofing weighing at least _____ per square.

    17. _____

    A. 15 lb.
    B. 30 lb.
    C. 45 lb.
    D. 55 lb.

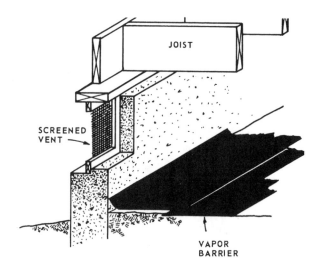

Name _____

18. One method of insulating the foundation wall of an existing structure is shown in the illustration below. Identify the materials and parts as specified.

18. A. _____

    B. _____

    C. _____

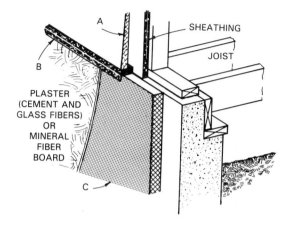

19. When warm, moist air is cooled, some of the moisture is released as condensation. The temperature at which this occurs for a given sample of air is called _____.

19. _____

20. A properly installed vapor barrier will protect walls, ceiling, and floor from moisture originating within a heated space. To be effective, the vapor barrier in an outside wall should be located _____.

20. _____

    A. on the outside of the sheathing
    B. between the sheathing and wall frame
    C. between the inside wall covering and wall frame
    D. on the outside surface of the insulation

21. Today, many residential structures are built on concrete slab floors that are insulated and contain a vapor barrier. Select the *incorrect* statement concerning this type of construction.

21. _____

    A. The vapor barrier must be continuous under the entire floor.
    B. Insulation can extend inward under the floor or be carried downward along the foundation.
    C. Both the insulation and vapor barrier should be continuous under the entire floor.
    D. Perimeter insulation is usually extended in from the foundation a horizontal distance of about 2'-0".

22. An unheated attic or space under a low pitched or flat roof should be ventilated. In a standard gable or hip roof design, soffit vents (as shown below) are commonly used. The total minimum area requirement is expressed as a fraction of the total ceiling area of the structure. The correct figure for the soffit vent shown is _____.

22. _____

    A. 1/300
    B. 1/500
    C. 1/900
    D. 1/1600

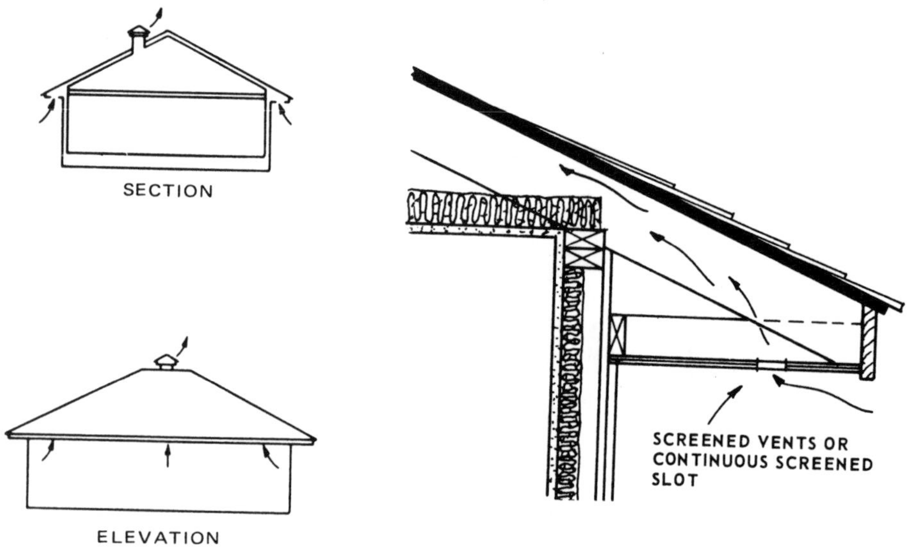

SECTION

ELEVATION

SCREENED VENTS OR CONTINUOUS SCREENED SLOT

23. The flanges of blanket insulation are stapled to either the face or side of the framing members. When attaching the flange to the inside edge of a stud, the staple should not be greater than _____.

23. _____

    A. 8″
    B. 12″
    C. 10″
    D. 16″

24. Perimeter insulation for a concrete slab floor requires a rigid material. A foamed plastic board commonly used is made from _____.

24. _____

    A. polyethylene
    B. polyurethane
    C. polystyrene
    D. polyester

Name _____

25. In the view below, fill insulation is being placed in the core of concrete blocks. This method of installation is called __(A)__. Another method of installing fill insulation is called __(B)__.

25. A. _____

B. _____

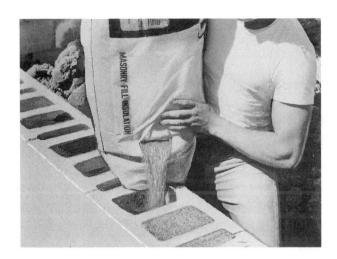

26. Estimate the number of square feet of area (walls and ceilings) to be insulated in the house plan shown below. Do not include the outside walls and ceiling of the garage. Round out any inch dimensions to a full foot. Deduct 60 sq. ft. for the sliding glass doors in the family room, but make no other allowances. Round out your answers to the next higher 10 sq. ft. (Make calculations in the space below.)

26. Walls: _____

Ceiling: _____

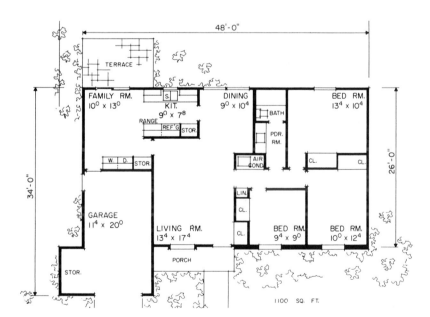

27. The unit of measure used to indicate the intensity or loudness of sound is called a(n) _____.

27. _____

28. Sound frequency is the rate at which sound energized air molecules vibrate. This frequency is measured in cycles per _____.

28. _____

29. The sound absorption quality of a material is expressed as the average percentage measured at several different frequencies. This value is abbreviated by the letters NRC which stand for _____.

    A. Noise Reduction Capacity
    B. Noise Reverberation Control
    C. Noise Reduction Coefficient
    D. Noise Reducing Capability

29. _____

30. As sound moves through any type of wall or other barrier, its intensity will be reduced. This reduction is called Sound Transmission Loss (TL). If a given sound of 75 dB is reduced to a level of 36 dB after passing through a wall, the TL rating of the wall would be _____.

30. _____

31. A modern system of rating the sound-blocking efficiency of a wall, floor, or ceiling has been established through extensive research. Values (called STC numbers) have been assigned to a wide range of structures and systems. The letters STC stand for _____.

    A. Standard Transmission Coefficient
    B. Systems Transmission Class
    C. Sound Transmission Capability
    D. Sound Transmission Class

31. _____

32. The drawings below show sectional views of a number of partitions that would be practical in residential construction. Provide the STC rating for each.

32. A. _____
    B. _____
    C. _____
    D. _____

1/2 IN. GYPSUM WALLBOARD

3/8 IN. GYPSUM LATH

1/2 IN. GYPSUM PLASTER

1/2 IN. SOUND DEADENING BD.

1/2 IN. GYPSUM WALLBOARD

1/2 IN. SOUND DEADENING BD.

1/2 IN. GYPSUM WALLBOARD LAMINATED AND PERIMETER SEALED

33. To secure the best possible soundproofing in a wall structure, consideration must be given to openings for convenience outlets, medicine cabinets, and recessed shelving. For example, convenience outlets and switch boxes on opposite faces of a partition should not be located in the same _____.

33. _____

Name _____

34. A standard hollow-core interior door that is carefully fitted will have a sound reduction value or transmission loss of about _____.   34. _____

    A. 20-25 dB
    B. 25-20 dB
    C. 30-35 dB
    D. 35-40 dB

35. The efficiency of an acoustical material is based on its ability to absorb sound waves. Some of the very best materials now available are designed to absorb up to _____ of the sound that strikes them.   35. _____

    A. 50%
    B. 60%
    C. 70%
    D. 80%

36. Acoustical materials may lose some of their efficiency if they are not properly maintained. When applying paint to perforated boards, it is best to use a _____.   36. _____

    A. spray gun
    B. soft-hair brush

37. Which one of the wall structures illustrated below has the lowest STC rating?   37. _____

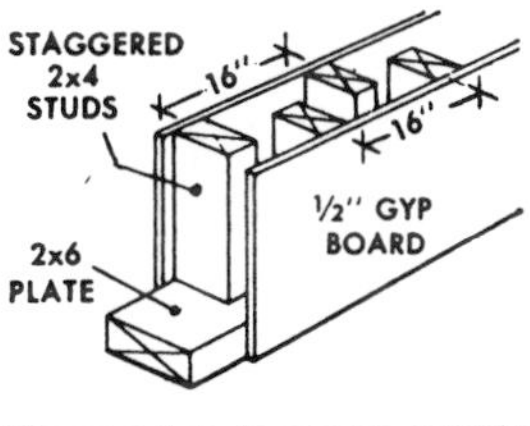

Staggered studs provide complete separation between wall faces. Staggering 2x3s on 2x4 plate is almost effective.

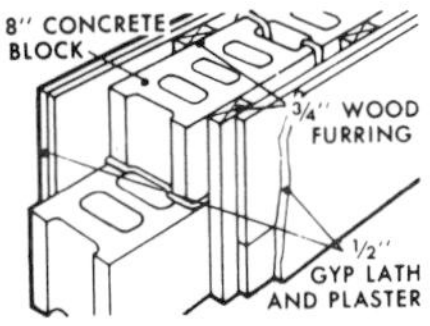

Concrete block with furred gypsum lath and plaster both sides has excellent properties in mid and high frequencies.

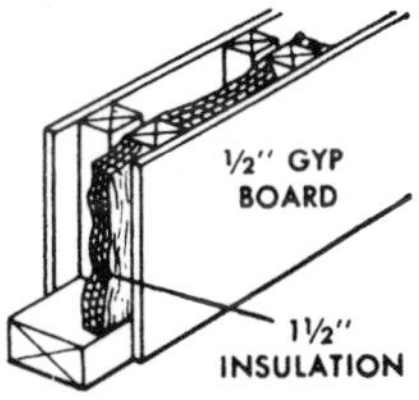

Slit-stud wall with 1 1/2'' blanket insulation hung from top plate.

A   B   C

38. Which one of the floor structures illustrated below will provide the highest STC rating?   38. _____

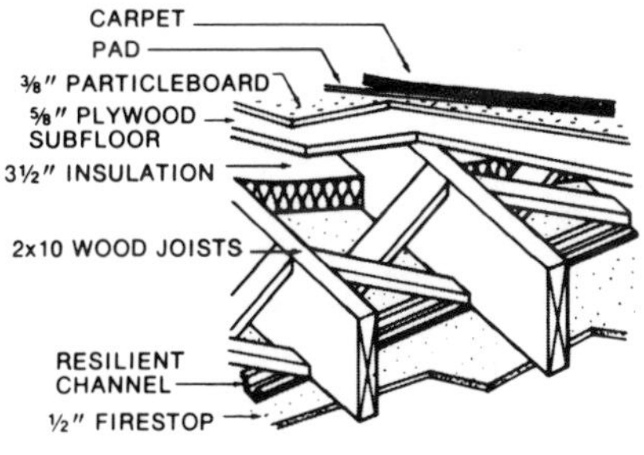

A 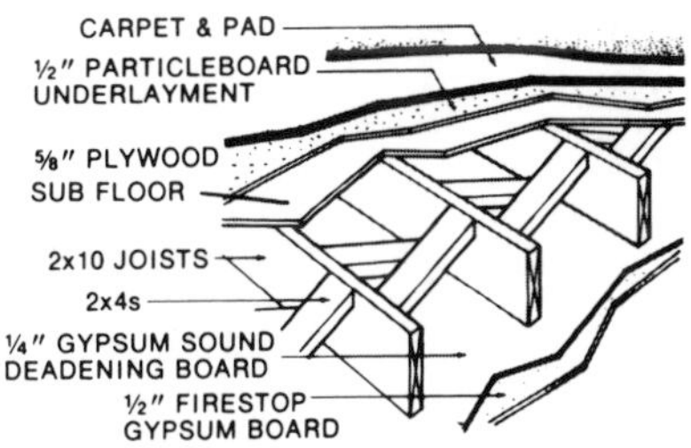   B

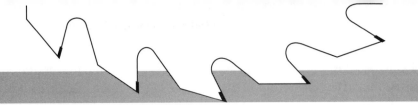

UNIT 15

Interior Wall and Ceiling Finish

Text Pages 429-462

Name _____

Date _____ Score _____

1. Gypsum wallboard is used for standard drywall construction. Panels are __(A)__ wide and lengths up to __(B)__ are generally available.

1. A. _____

   B. _____

2. In modern construction, wallboard panels are often attached with special screws. Since they hold the wallboard more securely than nails, ceiling spacing can be extended to a maximum of __(A)__ and side walls to __(B)__.

2. A. _____

   B. _____

3. In single layer drywall construction, the panels of gypsum board are applied directly to the wood frame as shown in the view below. Nail spacing should not exceed __(A)__ on the ceiling or be greater than __(B)__ on walls.

3. A. _____

   B. _____

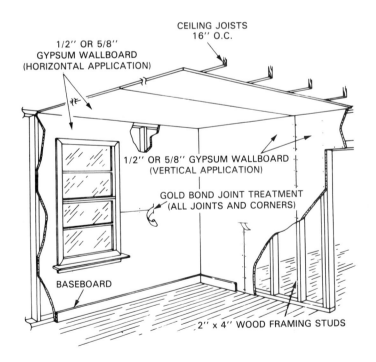

CEILING JOISTS
16'' O.C.

1/2'' OR 5/8''
GYPSUM WALLBOARD
(HORIZONTAL APPLICATION)

1/2'' OR 5/8'' GYPSUM WALLBOARD
(VERTICAL APPLICATION)

GOLD BOND JOINT TREATMENT
(ALL JOINTS AND CORNERS)

BASEBOARD

2'' x 4'' WOOD FRAMING STUDS

4. _____ is a fiber-reinforced panel material used as an underlayment for finishing materials used on walls, floors, and countertops.

4. _____

5. Backing board is a gypsum panel used as a base sheet in multilayer drywall construction. The 1/4″ and 3/8″ thicknesses have square edges. Backing board is also available in a 1/2″ thickness that has _____ edges.

    5. _____

    A. tapered
    B. beveled
    C. round
    D. T&G

6. In standard drywall construction, the edges of panels are tapered so that a special treatment can be applied to conceal the joints. A diagram of this treatment showing the coats and sequence of application is shown below. Identify the distances and items specified.

    6. A. _____
        B. _____
        C. _____
        D. _____

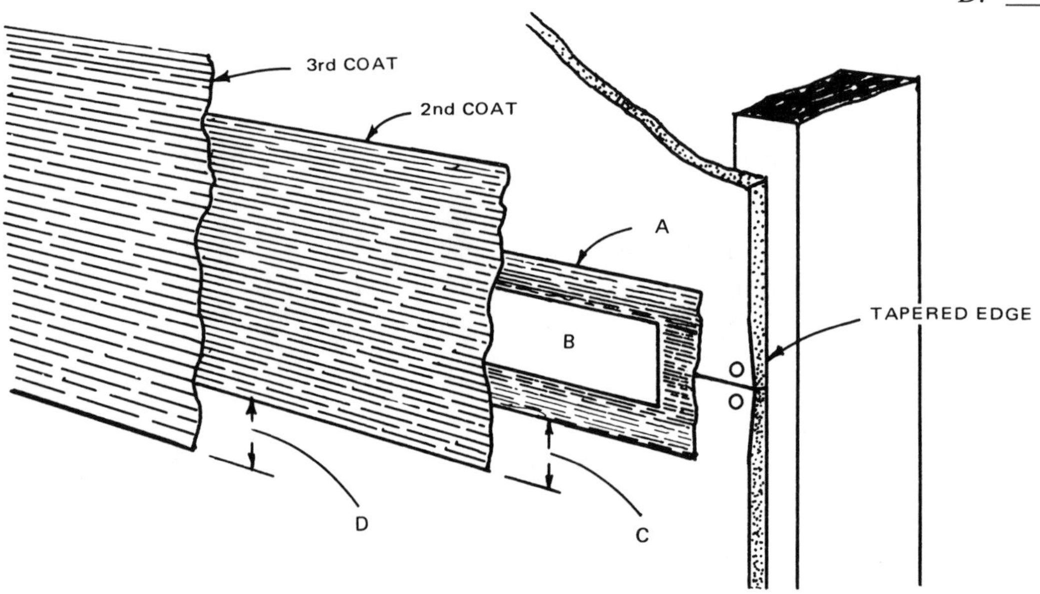

7. In double layer or two-ply construction, an adhesive is normally used to laminate the finish layer to the base layer. The finish layer is applied so that joints (either horizontal or vertical) are offset by a distance of at least _____ from those in the base layer.

    7. _____

    A. 8″
    B. 10″
    C. 12″
    D. 16″

8. A special gypsum wallboard that will withstand moisture is easily identified by its light _____ facing paper.

    8. _____

    A. blue
    B. gray
    C. green
    D. yellow

9. Veneer plaster is a high-strength material. It requires a minimum drying time of about _____ hours.

    9. _____

    A. 12
    B. 24
    C. 36
    D. 48

Name _____

10. The illustration below shows the installation of corner bead for single coat application of veneer plaster. The bead should be set for a _____ thickness.

    10. _____

    A. 1/16″
    B. 3/32″
    C. 1/8″
    D. 3/16″

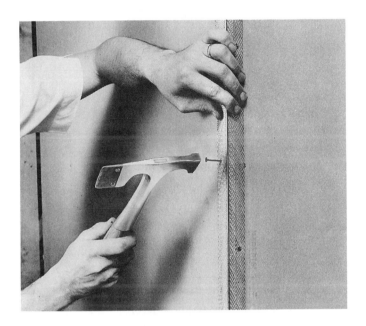

11. Shown below are special molding strips often used to install predecorated gypsum panels. Which of the following procedures should be followed when using this type of molding?

    11. _____

    A. Space, plumb, and apply the molding and then attach the panels.
    B. Secure the panels to the surface with adhesive and then apply the moldings.
    C. Moldings and panels are applied to the surface at the same time.

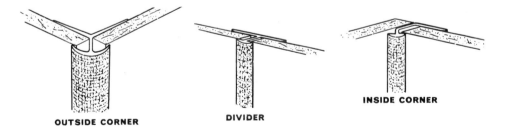

OUTSIDE CORNER   DIVIDER   INSIDE CORNER

12. Plywood panels should be conditioned to the space or room in which they will be installed. This means that both faces of each panel should be exposed to the air and temperature of the space for at least _____ before the installation is made.

    12. _____

13. Solid wood paneling, at the time of installation, should have about the same MC as it will attain after the structure is occupied. For most parts of the country, this will be about _____.

    13. _____

    A. 6% to 8%
    B. 8% to 10%
    C. 10% to 12%
    D. 12% to 15%

14. Instead of using furring strips, plywood panels may be bonded to a base layer of gypsum wallboard securely nailed to studding. Which one of the following statements is *incorrect* concerning this type of installation when located on an outside wall?

    14. _____

    A. Eliminates the need for vapor barrier.
    B. Helps align bowed and crooked studs.
    C. Adds rigidity to the surface.
    D. Improves fire resistant qualities.

15. Where a paneling installation is subjected to unusually hard wear in public or commercial buildings, prefabricated panels consisting of plastic laminate surfaces are frequently specified. The thickness of the plastic laminate bonded to these basic panels is usually to _____. (Choose two.)

    15. _____

            _____

    A. 1/32"
    B. 1/16"
    C. 3/32"
    D. 1/8"

16. When making a vertical installation of solid wood paneling consisting of nominal 1" tongue and groove boards, nailing or furring strips are required at the top and bottom with intermediate strips spaced no further than _____ apart.

    16. _____

    A. 24"
    B. 32"
    C. 36"
    D. 48"

17. Plaster requires some kind of a base upon which the plaster can be spread. A commonly used base is gypsum lath which is available in a standard panel size of _____.

    17. _____

    A. 12×32
    B. 12×48
    C. 16×32
    D. 16×48

18. Insulating fiberboard lath is available in widths up to 24" and a maximum thickness of _____.

    18. _____

    A. 3/8"
    B. 7/16"
    C. 1/2"
    D. 5/8"

Name _____

19. When making an installation of 3/8″ gypsum lath, which of the following specifications is *not* correct?

    19. _____

    A. Lath must be nailed at every stud or joist crossing.
    B. Use a No. 13 ga. nail with a minimum length of 1″.
    C. Nails should not be closer than 3/8″ to ends and edges.
    D. When using staples, the crown should be parallel to the long dimension of the framing member.

20. To control plaster coat thickness and provide a level surface or edge, wood or metal strips are attached to doors and other openings. These strips are generally called plaster _____.

    20. _____

21. A gypsum lath installation must be reinforced in certain areas and at inside and outside corners. Identify the reinforcing items in the drawings below.

    21. A. _____

    B. _____

    C. _____

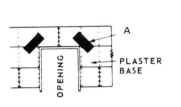

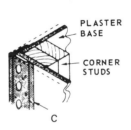

22. In the view below, 1 × 2 material is being attached to a concrete block wall to serve as a nailing base for gypsum lath. The strips are generally called _____.

    22. _____

23. Cement board, illustrated below, is a relatively new product with uses for both interiors and exteriors. Which of the following statements is *not* correct?

23. _____

    A. Does not withstand moisture well.
    B. Should be worked with tungsten carbide cutting/sawing/drilling tools.
    C. Usually consists of a fiberglass reinforced mix of cement.
    D. Is fireproof and resists impact.

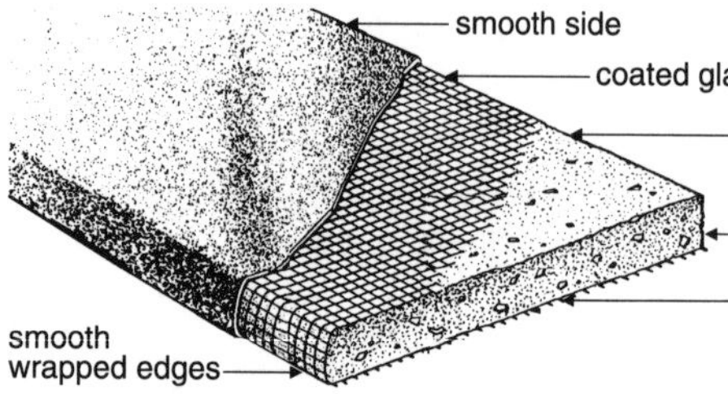

smooth side
coated glass-fiber mesh
aggregated portland cement core
cut edge
rough textured side
smooth wrapped edges

UNITED STATES GYPSUM CO.

24. In standard three coat plaster applications, the first coat is called the __(A)__ and is applied directly to the plaster base. The second coat, which is carefully leveled, is generally referred to as the __(B)__.

24. A. _____

    B. _____

25. In standard plastering applications, which of the following statements is *incorrect*?

25. _____

    A. In most residential plastering the first two coats are applied almost simultaneously.
    B. Minimum plaster thickness (including all coats) should not be less than 1/2″ when applied over regular gypsum lath.
    C. When plaster is applied to metal lath, the total thickness measured from the backside of the lath should be not less than 3/4″.
    D. A 1/2″ thickness of plaster has almost twice the resistance to bending or breaking as a 3/8″ thickness.

26. Solid paneling installed horizontally does not require furring strips. True or False?

26. _____

27. Ceiling tiles are often used in remodeling work since they can be applied to nearly any surface. Which one of the following would be of least importance in selecting a given product?

27. _____

    A. appearance
    B. unit weight
    C. fire resistance
    D. light reflection
    E. cost
    F. installation procedures

Name _____

28. Some ceiling tiles are designed with special tongue and grove joints that makes them easy to apply with staples. Identify the parts of the joint shown below.

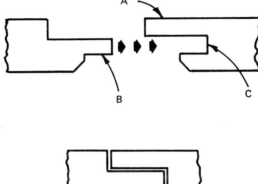

ASSEMBLED

28. A. _____

    B. _____

    C. _____

29. When installing furring strips to exposed joists where several of the joists extend below the plane of the others, it is best to _____.

    A. use tapered wedges between joists and strips
    B. plane off the lower edge of the joist
    C. cut notches in lower edge of low joists
    D. use a double layer of furring strips

29. _____

30. Calculate the amount of 1 × 6 tongue and groove solid wood paneling needed for one wall of a room 23′ long with an 8′ height. There are no openings and the boards will be applied vertically. Use the area factor listed on page 461 of the text and add 7% for waste. Round out your answer to the next higher full board foot. (Make your calculations in the space below.)

30. bd. ft.: _____

31. When making an installation of ceiling tile using an adhesive or staples, the best procedure is to start setting the tile _____.

    A. in any one of the corners
    B. along the main centerline of the room
    C. at a midpoint on either wall
    D. at the center of an end wall

31. _____

32. The illustration below shows a patented ceiling system using clips to secure panels. It is known as the _____ _____ system.

32. _____

33. How many 4 × 8 sheets of plywood will be required to panel the wall described in question 30. The panels would be applied vertically, and the studs are all equally spaced 16″ O.C. (Make your calculations in the space below.)

33. No. of panels: _____

Sq. ft. of
plywood: _____

34. Determine the amount of standard gypsum lath for a building with 1140 sq. ft. of floor area. The total length of all inside wall surfaces is 362′ and the ceiling is 8′ high. Make no allowances for doors and windows, and round out your answer to the nearest full bundle of lath. (Make your calculations in the space below.)

34. Sq. ft.: _____

Bundles of lath: _____

Name _____

35. Plasterers base their price estimates on the total number of square yards. Figure the square yards of plaster needed for the structure in Problem 34 and round out your answer to next higher sq. yd. (Make your calculations in the space below.)

35. _____

36. An 8′ ceiling measures 13′-7″ by 20′-8″. How many standard 12 × 12 tiles will be required to cover the ceiling if a balanced pattern (both lengthwise and crosswise) is specified? How many standard cartons must be ordered if no other matching tile are available? (Make your calculations in the space below.)

36. No. of tile: _____

No. of cartons: _____

UNIT 16

Finish Flooring

Text Pages 463-482

Name _____

Date _____ Score _____

1. Species of hardwood commonly used for finish flooring in residential construction include oak, maple, beech, and _birch_

   A. elm
   B. ash
   C. birch
   D. spruce

   1. _C_

2. The drawing below shows typical hardwood strip flooring. Identify the items specified.

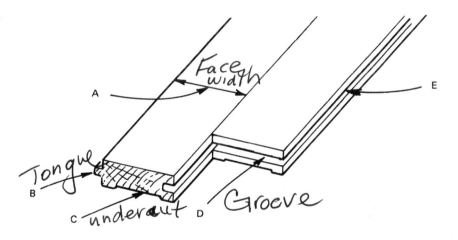

2. A. _face width_
   B. _tongue_
   C. _undercut_
   D. _Groove_
   E. _____

3. Hardwood flooring is generally available in thicknesses of 3/8″, 1/2″, and _____.

   A. 5/16″
   B. 7/16″
   C. 3/4″
   D. 25/32″

   3. _3/4″_

4. The best grade of plain-sawed oak flooring is designated by the term _____.

   A. first
   B. clear
   C. select
   D. premium

   4. _____

? ,

5. When installing standard strip flooring (3/8″ × 2″) use 4d casing nails and space them ___ apart.

   A. 8″
   B. 10″
   C. 12″
   D. 16″

5. _8″_

6. What type of tool is being used in the illustration below to install strip flooring?

6. _Portable nailer_

BULLARD-HAVEN TECHNICAL

7. A hardwood flooring installation may start along a side wall as shown below. The first strip is carefully aligned and then nailed. Identify the types of nailing and provide the recommended spacing and angles.

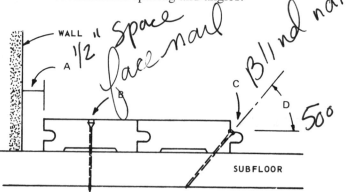

WALL
A ½″ Space
face nail
C Blind nail
D 50°
SUBFLOOR

7. A. _____
   B. _____
   C. _____
   D. _____

8. When installing strip flooring, it is recommended that end joints be spaced a minimum of _____ apart in adjacent courses.

   A. 6″
   B. 8″
   C. 12″
   D. 16″

8. _____

9. To reverse the direction of laying in some section of the installation, a groove can be converted into a tongue by inserting a hardwood strip. This strip is commonly referred to as a _____.

9. _____

Name _____

10. Determine the amount of 3/4″ × 4 1/4″ strip flooring required for a room 17′ × 28′. Refer to the table on page 468. Provide the number of board feet and the number of full bundles required. (Make your calculations in the space below.)

10. Bd. ft.: _____

Bundles: _____

11. Calculate the amount of 3/8″ × 2″ strip flooring needed for a living room (14′ × 24′) and an entrance hall (4′ × 10′). Provide the total number of board feet required for the two areas and the total number of full bundles that should be ordered. (Make your calculations in the space below.)

11. Bd. ft.: _____

Bundles: _____

12. Hardwood strip flooring (3/4″) can be installed over a concrete slab. An approved system, where the concrete is in contact with the ground, is shown in the drawing below. The vapor barriers are polyethylene film. Identify these and other items as specified.

12. A. _____

B. _____

C. _____

D. _____

E. _____

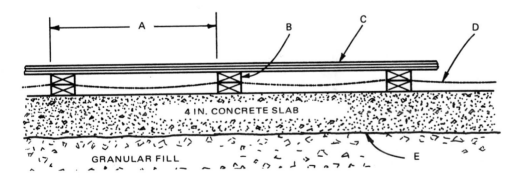

13. A variety of wood block flooring is available and is generally installed with a mastic or adhesive. Today, most wood block floors are prefinished. Which of the following statements concerning prefinished wood floors is *incorrect*?

13. _____

A. The finish is superior to that which is normally applied on the job.
B. Special care and accuracy must be maintained when making the installation.
C. Time is saved since prefinished units can be butted directly against baseboards.
D. Floors are ready for service immediately after the installation is completed.

14. Conventional subflooring must be covered with an underlayment before the installation of resilient floor tile. Hardboard panels are often used for this purpose and should be "conditioned" to the space where they will be applied for at least _____ hours.

    A. 24
    B. 36
    C. 48
    D. 60

14. _____

15. When plywood is used for underlayment, the grain of the panels should run at a right angle to the floor joists. Field spacing of nails for a 1/4″ thickness should not be greater than __(A)__. The nail pattern along edges of the panels should not be greater than __(B)__.

15. A. _____

    B. _____

16. The underlayment surface for resilient materials such as vinyl, rubber, and linoleum must be smooth. Over a period of time, even the slightest irregularities will show on the surface of the tile. This transfer from the base surface to the finish surface is commonly referred to as _____.

16. _____

17. The view below shows hardboard underlayment being stapled to the subfloor. Nails or staples should be spaced 3/8″ from the edge of the panels. The panels should be fitted together carefully with a __(A)__ space at each joint. When nails are used for the installation they should be cement coated or __(B)__.

17. A. _____

    B. _____

18. To check the right angles formed by the main centerlines of a room layout, you can use a framing square or set up a right triangle with a base of 4′, an altitude of _____, and a hypotenuse of _____.

    A. 2′   D. 5′
    B. 3′   E. 6′
    C. 4′   F. 7′

18. _____

_____

Name _____

19. The adhesive is spread evenly over the surface with a trowel or brush according to the manufacturer's recommendations. Generally it is best to make the first spread over _____ of the total area.

    19. _____

    A. one-eighth
    B. one-fourth
    C. one-half
    D. three-fourths

20. Self-adhering tiles can be installed over an existing floor. It is very important that the surface be smooth and free of _____, grease, and dirt.

    20. _____

21. Flexible vinyl flooring is fastened down only along edges and seams. It is generally available in a width of _____.

    21. _____

    A. 8′
    B. 9′
    C. 10′
    D. 12′

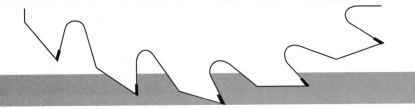

UNIT 17

Stair Construction

Text Pages 483-500

Name _____

Date _____ Score _____

1. In the normal sequence of construction, main stairways are built or installed after interior wall surfaces are complete and finished flooring or _____ has been laid.

1. _____

2. There are several ways to describe or classify a stair. One way is to indicate whether or not it is enclosed by walls. With this in mind, identify the stair drawings below.

2. A. _____

B. _____

C. _____

D. _____

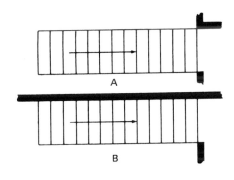

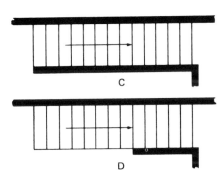

3. The size of the rough opening for a stairwell must be known or calculated during the rough framing of a structure. Members (trimmers and headers) around the opening should be doubled whenever they are longer than _____.

3. _____

    A. 4′
    B. 6′
    C. 8′
    D. 10′

4. Main supporting members (called stringers or carriages) run from one level to the next. Other basic parts and stair terms are included in the drawing below. Identify each one specified.

4. A. _____

   B. _____

   C. _____

   D. _____

   E. _____

   F. _____

   G. _____

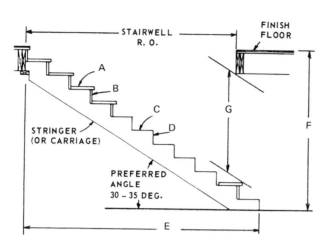

5. Stair angle or slope is determined by the rise-run combination. The preferred angle for a standard stair is in the range of _____.

   A. 20° to 25°
   B. 25° to 30°
   C. 30° to 35°
   D. 35° to 40°

5. _____

6. The relationship or size ratio between risers and treads is very important in stair design. One commonly accepted rule states that the sum of two risers plus one tread should equal _____ inches.

   A. 18 to 20
   B. 20 to 22
   C. 24 to 25
   D. 25 to 26

6. _____

7. If a given stair has a riser 6 3/4″ high, the correct width of the tread (less nosing) should be _____. Apply the rule referred to in item No. 6. (Make your calculations in the space below.)

   A. 10 1/2″ to 11″
   B. 11 1/2″ to 12 1/2″
   C. 13 1/2″ to 14″

7. _____

8. A minimum total width of 3′ is generally recommended for a main stairway. FHA regulations permit a minimum width (clear of the handrail) of _____.

   A. 2′-6″
   B. 2′-8″
   C. 2′-10″
   D. 2′-11″

8. _____

Name _____

9. Except for very wide stairs, a handrail on one side or the other is satisfactory. The drawing below shows the position of a handrail attached to a wall. Provide the recommended heights specified.

9. A. _____

   B. _____

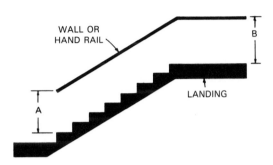

10. Calculate the number and size of risers and treads for a main stairway (straight run) for a residence. The vertical distance between the finished surface of the two floors is 8'-11" and the riser height must not be greater than 7 1/2". Use the "riser-tread" rule used in item No. 6. (Make your calculations in the space below.)

10. No. of risers: _____

   Riser height: _____

   No. of treads: _____

   Tread width: _____

11. Using the figures developed in the previous problem, determine the total run of the stairs. (Make your calculations in the space below.)

11. Total run: _____

12. Before making the actual layout of a stair stringer, the calculated riser height is laid out and checked on a straight strip called a _____.

12. _____

13. When all the risers and treads have been laid out on the stringer stock, an adjustment must be made for the thickness of the tread. This is best accomplished by _____.

13. _____

   A. relocating each tread line downward by an amount equal to tread thickness

   B. extending the top riser and shortening the bottom riser by an amount equal to tread thickness

   C. shortening the bottom riser by an amount equal to the tread thickness

14. Nosing is an important part of a stair tread. In typical construction they range in width from 1 1/8″ to __(A)__. As a general rule, when the basic width of a tread is increased, the nosing width is __(B)__ (increased, decreased).

14. A. _____

B. _____

15. Identify the three basic types of riser designs shown below.

15. A. _____

B. _____

C. _____

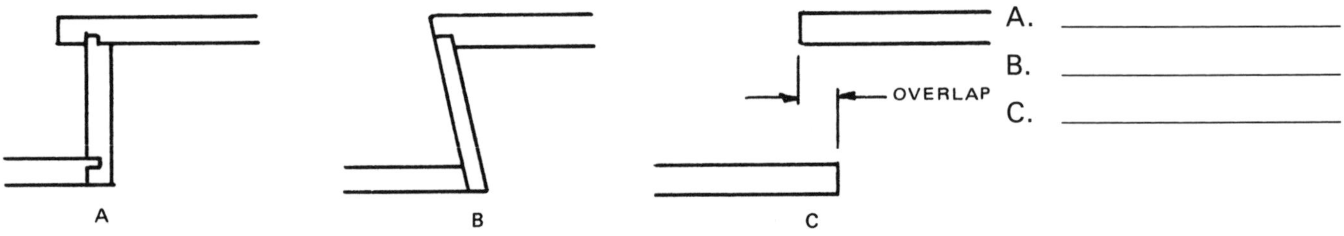

A. _____

B. _____

C. _____

16. The simplest type of stringers are formed by attaching cleats on which the treads can rest. Another method consists of cutting dados into which the treads will fit. Depth of the dados should equal _____ of the stringer thickness.

A. one-fourth
B. one-third
C. one-half
D. five-eighths

16. _____

17. When a cutout stringer is attached (using nails or screws) to a backing stringer the assembly is generally referred to as a _____ stringer.

17. _____

18. In the highest quality of stair construction, tapered grooves are cut into the stringer. Treads and risers are inserted into these grooves and held in place with glue and wedges. The standard taper used for these wedges is _____ per foot.

A. 1/4″
B. 3/8″
C. 1/2″
D. 3/4″

18. _____

19. Winder stairs have a tapered tread in the section where the direction of the run is changed. It is recommended that the center of convergence of this taper be located _____ the stair construction.

19. _____

Name _____

20. Main stairs that are open on one or both sides usually have a decorative structure that supports the handrail. This assembly is generally called a balustrade. In the view below, identify the parts of a balustrade and other items specified.

20. A. _____

   B. _____

   C. _____

   D. _____

   E. _____

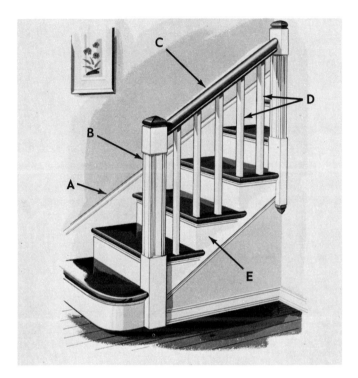

21. High quality handrail sections are joined together with a special concealed bolt and nut. The nut is properly tightened by using a(n) _____ and _____. (Choose two.)

   A. open-end wrench
   B. screwdriver
   C. nail set and hammer
   D. hammer claw

21. _____

   _____

22. Which part of a balustrade must be securely attached to the starter step or anchored to the building frame?

   A. Open stringer.
   B. Baluster.
   C. Newel.
   D. Bracket.

22. _____

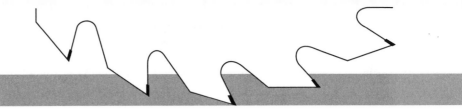

UNIT 18

Doors and Interior Trim

Text Pages 501-526

Name _____

Date _____ Score _____

1. Moldings are shaped strips of wood used to trim or connect various elements. Door casing, for example, connects the jamb to the wall surface. Shown below are typical moldings used for interior trim. Identify each item as specified.

A B C D

E F

G H

1. A. _____
   B. _____
   C. _____
   D. _____
   E. _____
   F. _____
   G. _____
   H. _____

2. Standard interior door jambs for plastered walls in residential structures are 3/4″ thick and _____ wide.

2. _____

   A. 4 7/8″
   B. 5″
   C. 5 1/4″
   D. 5 3/8″

3. Side jambs are usually cut so they will measure _____ below the head jamb. This length will provide for clearance under the door. Excess can be trimmed off.

3. _____

4. To assemble a door frame, side jambs are nailed to the head jamb. For this operation, use _____ casing or box nails.

4. _____

   A. 6d
   B. 7d
   C. 8d
   D. 10d

5. The two general types of doors are panel and flush. The standard thickness of exterior residential doors is __(A)__. Interior passage doors are normally __(B)__ thick.

5. A. _____

    B. _____

6. The drawing below shows a section through a door jamb. Provide the measurement specified and identify the parts.

6. A. _____

    B. _____

    C. _____

    D. _____

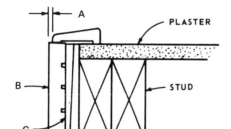

7. When using a miter joint between side and head casing for a door, which of the following installation procedures and requirements would be *incorrect*?

7. _____

  A. Hold the side pieces in place and mark the position of the miter joint at the top.
  B. Use a miter box or wood trimmer to cut the joint.
  C. Attach the side casings temporarily and then lay out and cut the head casing.
  D. Use 8d casing or finish nails to secure the casing to the jamb and space them about 10″ apart.

8. Panel doors consist of stiles, rails, and panels. The panels are made from plywood, hardboard, or thin solid stock. After the door is installed, the rails are in a __(A)__ position and the stiles are in a __(B)__ position.

8. A. _____

    B. _____

  A. horizontal
  B. vertical
  C. diagonal

Name _____

9. The illustration below shows two kinds of flush doors. One has a solid core, the other a hollow core. Identify the parts as specified.

9. A. _____

   B. _____

   C. _____

   D. _____

   E. _____

   F. _____

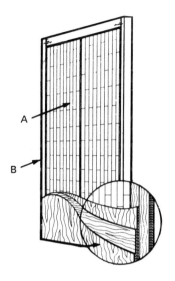 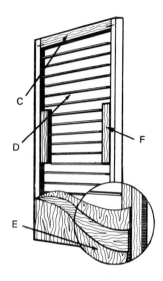

10. Doors are designed to fit standard size openings and should not be cut to fit smaller openings. Cutouts for glass inserts in flush doors should not be more than _____ of the face area.

    10. _____

    A. 30%
    B. 40%
    C. 50%
    D. 60%

11. In the illustration below, a power plane is being used to trim a door to size. Recommended clearances for an interior door include: lock side __(A)__, hinge side __(B)__, top __(C)__, bottom __(D)__.

    11. A. _____

1/16″	3/16″
3/32″	1/2″
1/8″	5/8″

    B. _____

    C. _____

    D. _____

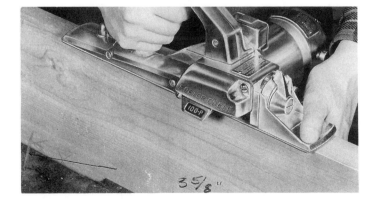

12. After the door has been trimmed to fit the opening, a bevel is planed on the lock side. This bevel should be about _____ (slightly greater for narrow doors and slightly less for wide doors).

    A. 2°
    B. 2 1/2°
    C. 3°
    D. 3 1/2°

12. _____

13. Gains for hinges are usually cut with an electric router guided by a door-and-jamb template. The top hinge is spaced _____ in from the ends of the door. The bottom hinge is spaced in from the ends of the door a distance of _____.

    A. 6″
    B. 7″
    C. 8″
    D. 10″
    E. 11″
    F. 12″

13. Top hinge. _____

    Bottom hinge. _____

14. After the door and hinges have been mounted on the jamb and checked for proper clearance, the stops are installed. With the door in a closed position, the clearance of the stop on the hinged side should be _____.

    A. 1/32″
    B. 1/16″
    C. 3/32″
    D. 1/8″

14. _____

15. Provide the correct name for the four types of passage door locks shown below.

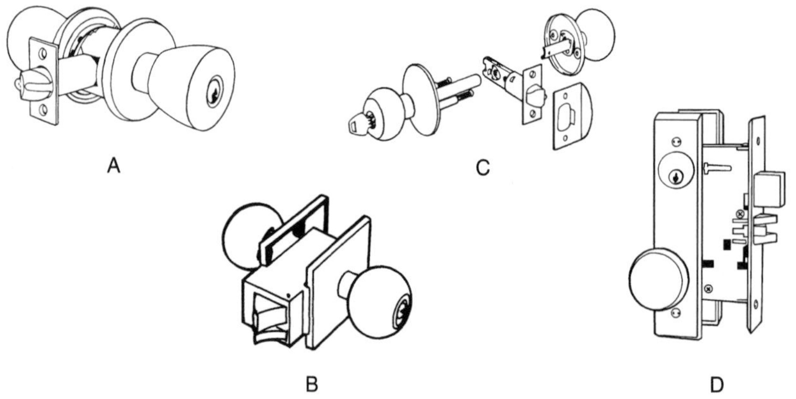

15. A. _____

    B. _____

    C. _____

    D. _____

A   C

B   D

16. To provide extra security, outside doors are often equipped with a special lock. This lock, which may be keyed from both sides, is called a(n) _____.

16. _____

Name _____

17. When ordering locks, it may be necessary to specify the swing of the door. This is determined by facing the outside of the door. Determine the swing (the hand of the door) for the four drawings below. Give your answer in the accepted abbreviations of LHR, RH, RHR, and LH.

17. A. _____

    B. _____

    C. _____

    D. _____

   A   B   C   D

18. Passage door locks are normally installed in the door a vertical distance of _____ above the finished floor. This distance is measured to the centerline of the knob.

18. _____

19. The positions of centerlines for holes that must be bored to mount cylindrical locks are laid out with _____ furnished by the manufacturer.

    A. templates
    B. boring jigs
    C. spacers
    D. patterns

19. _____

20. Identify the main parts (as specified) of the passage door lock set shown below.

20. A. _____

    B. _____

    C. _____

    D. _____

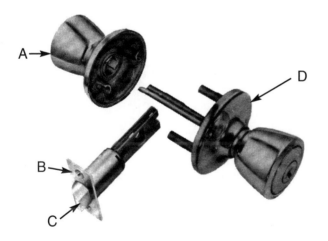

21. One type of sliding door requires the installation of track during the rough framing. This type of door is commonly referred to as a(n) _____.

21. _____

22. A folding door commonly used on closets and wardrobes, consists of a pair of doors hinged together. Doors of this type are commonly called _____ units.

22. _____

23. The illustration below shows a cutaway view of track and rollers for sliding doors. This type of sliding door installation is called a _____ unit.

23. _____

24. Multipanel folding doors are constructed from narrow panels that are hinged along the edges. As the door is opened, panels fold together, forming a _____.

24. _____

    A. bundle
    B. deck
    C. pack
    D. stack

25. The drawing below shows the inside view of a pair of standard double-hung windows. Identify the inside trim members as specified.

25. A. _____

    B. _____

    C. _____

    D. _____

    E. _____

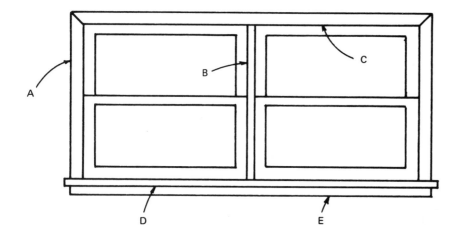

Name _____

26. When installing standard interior window trim, the usual procedure is to apply the _(A)_ last. Its length should be equal to the distance between the outside edges of the _(B)_ .

26. A. _____

    B. _____

27. Baseboards cover the joints between the wall surface and floor. Identify the type of joints recommended at corners and intersections as indicated in the drawing below.

27. A. _____

    B. _____

    C. _____

    D. _____

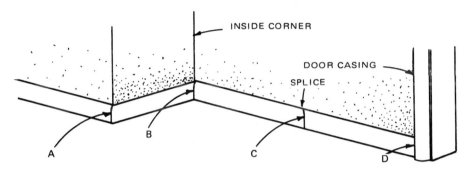

UNIT 19

Cabinetmaking

Text Pages 527-556

Name _____

Date _____ Score _____

1. In building construction, the term cabinetwork refers to such items as kitchen cabinets, bathroom cabinets, and wardrobes. The term "built-in" means that the unit is located within or _____ to the structure.

1. _____

2. When cabinets are built on the job, the selection of kind and sizes of joints is usually the responsibility of the _____.
   A. architect
   B. owner
   C. contractor
   D. carpenter

2. _____

3. In kitchen cabinet design, the bottom of a wall cabinet is usually located from 15″ to 18″ above the top surface of the base cabinet. FHA specifies a minimum distance of _____ when the wall cabinet is located over a sink or cooking unit.
   A. 20″
   B. 24″
   C. 26″
   D. 28″

3. _____

4. The term "in-the-white" means that the factory-built cabinet is _____.

   A. finished in white enamel
   B. finished in a "pickled" stain and coated with a clear satin varnish
   C. assembled but not finished

4. _____

5. The illustration below shows three standard types of cabinet door catches. Provide the correct name for each type.

5. A. _____
   B. _____
   C. _____

A

B

C

6. Refer to illustrations A and B below and indicate the style of cabinet construction for each.

6. A. _____

   B. _____

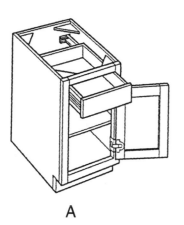

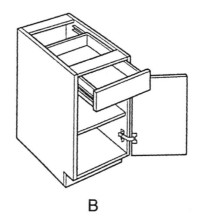

A   B

7. The drawings below show a section view of a kitchen cabinet, a bathroom cabinet and a closet with sliding doors. Provide the recommended sizes as specified.

7. A. _____

   B. _____

   C. _____

   D. _____

   E. _____

   F. _____

   G. _____

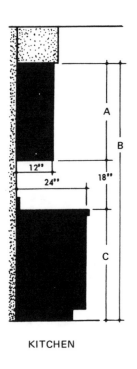

KITCHEN

BATHROOM CABINET

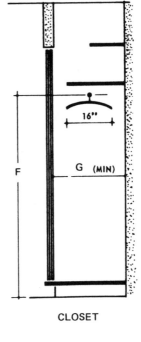

CLOSET

138

Name _____

8. A partial group of standard wall units produced by a kitchen cabinet manufacturer is shown below. Secure the overall dimensions for the unit numbers listed in the answer column. List the cabinet size in order: W × H × D.

8. No. 3012: _____

No. 2730: _____

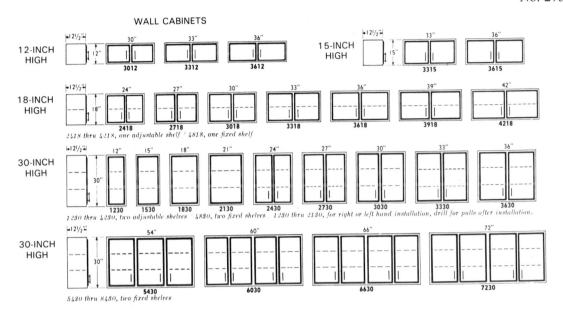

WALL CABINETS

9. When installing factory-built wall cabinet units, hanging strips should be securely attached to stud framing with screws. Where studs or other framing members are inaccessible, the use of _____ bolts is recommended.

9. _____

10. The installation of new factory-built kitchen cabinets is often included in a remodeling project. From the list below, select the step or procedure that is *incorrect* in making an installation of base cabinets.

10. _____

    A. Remove baseboard from walls where cabinets will be located.

    B. Starting at a corner, locate cabinets in proper position and fasten them together.

    C. Fit the countertop into position and attach it to the cabinets before cabinets are fastened to wall.

    D. Start at the highest point in the floor and level the front edges of all cabinets after they have been fastened together.

11. Since floors are rarely level and walls seldom plumb, _____ and _____ are used on walls and floors so that cabinets do not become wracked or twisted during installation.

11. _____

_____

12. The carpenter prepares a full-sized drawing (usually a section view) showing the location of drawers, shelves, doors, and framing details. This drawing is generally referred to as a _____.

12. _____

13. The drawing below shows an exploded view of parts and joints commonly used in a base cabinet when it is built as a separate unit. Identify the specified items.

13. A. _____

B. _____

C. _____

D. _____

E. _____

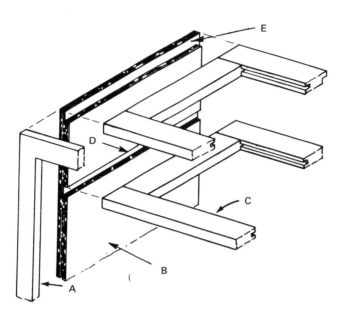

14. Facing strips are applied to the front of the basic cabinet frame. The vertical members are called stiles and the horizontal members are called _____.

14. _____

15. When constructing a base cabinet (see illustration below) by an assembled-in-place procedure, which one of the following would be *incorrect*?

15. _____

   A. All full partitions are notched at the back top corner.
   B. End panels are installed after the bottom is attached to the base.
   C. The 2 × 4 base should be made perfectly level by using shims.
   D. Layout lines can be made directly on the floor and wall.

16. In the application of facing strips to assembled-in-place cabinets, which one of the following statements would be *incorrect*?

16. _____

   A. Each piece is marked and installed separately.
   B. The length is laid out while holding it in place on the cabinet.
   C. Marked piece should not be used to lay out duplicate parts.
   D. Parts are glued and nailed in place with finishing nails.

Name _____

17. When a dado or gain is used to assemble facing strips, the depth is usually made _____ or slightly less so the joint will be covered by the lip of doors or drawers.

17. _____

    A. 3/16″
    B. 1/4″
    C. 3/8″
    D. 1/2″

18. Identify the three basic types of drawer guides shown in the illustration below.

18. A. _____

    B. _____

    C. _____

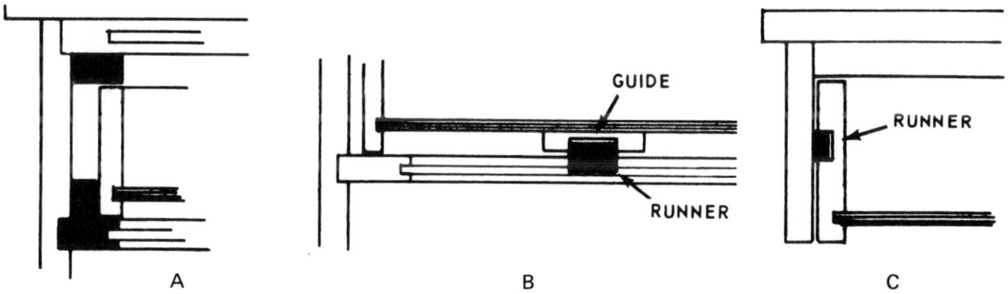

GUIDE

RUNNER

RUNNER

A   B   C

19. In some drawer guide arrangements it may be necessary to install a strip or strips somewhere over the drawer to prevent it from tilting downward when it is open. A strip or unit that serves this specific function is referred to as a _____.

19. _____

    A. kicker
    B. guider
    C. leveler
    D. baluster

20. Several different kinds of joints are used to assemble the various parts of a cabinet drawer. Because of the extra strain usually encountered, the strongest joints should be used to assemble the _____.

20. _____

    A. front and bottom
    B. bottom and sides
    C. sides and back
    D. front and sides

21. Lipped drawers are commonly used for kitchen cabinets. To form a lipped drawer front, rabbets are cut along the _____.

21. _____

    A. top and bottom edge
    B. edge of both sides
    C. top, bottom, and sides
    D. top and sides

22. In drawer building, it is usually recommended that the drawer _____ be cut out first.

    22. _____

    A. front
    B. sides
    C. back
    D. bottom

23. The partial drawings below show a top view of the right front corner of a drawer. Complete each view, showing an approved type of joint. (3 Points For Correct Answer)

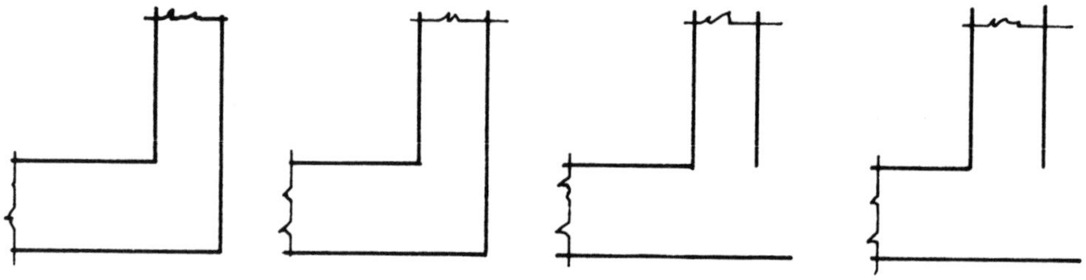

24. When wood or metal pins are used to support adjustable shelves, it is recommended that the holes for the pins be drilled _____ (before, after) the basic cabinet is assembled.

    24. _____

25. Standard shelving that is 3/4″ thick should be carried on supports that are spaced not more than _____ apart.

    25. _____

    A. 32″
    B. 36″
    C. 40″
    D. 42″

26. Two general classifications of built-in cabinet doors are sliding and swinging. Identify the three types of swinging doors shown below.

    26. A. _____
          B. _____
          C. _____

A   B   C

27. When standard butt hinges are used to install a cabinet door, they are usually mounted in a cutout called a _____.

    27. _____

    A. rabbet
    B. recess
    C. gain
    D. router

Name _____

28. Sliding doors are usually designed so that they can be removed from the opening by _____.

    28. _____

    A. removing a stop along the top edge
    B. raising the door and pulling the lower edge outward
    C. removing a strip at either end of the track
    D. disconnecting the track and pulling it outward

29. Plastic laminates commonly used for the surface of cabinet counters and tops is _____ thick.

    29. _____

    A. 1/32″
    B. 1/16″
    C. 3/32″
    D. 1/8″

30. On-the-job installations of plastic laminates are normally made with an adhesive called _____.

    30. _____

    A. urea resin glue
    B. contact bond cement
    C. polyvinyl glue
    D. casein waterproof glue

31. Architectural Woodworking Institute Standards specify that a backing sheet of plastic laminate be used on any unsupported area of counters or tops that exceed _____.

    31. _____

    A. 2 sq. ft.
    B. 3 sq. ft.
    C. 4 sq. ft.
    D. 6 sq. ft.

32. Trimming and smoothing the edges of a plastic laminate application is an important operation. The recommended angle of the slight bevel between a top and side surface is about _____.

    32. _____

    A. 15°
    B. 20°
    C. 30°
    D. 35°

33. Drawer pulls are often located slightly _____ (above, below) the centerline of the drawer front.

    33. _____

34. The carpenter should establish an appropriate schedule for the delivery of cabinets and interior finish materials. If delivered too far ahead of schedule they will interfere with other work and may be subjected to _____.

34. _____

35. The drawing below illustrates steps to be taken for proper installation of cabinets so that they are not wracked by uneven surfaces. Match the steps to the letters on the drawing by placing the numbers in the corresponding blanks.

1. Check space for tall unit by measuring up from high point level.
2. Remove plaster at high points.
3. Strike level base line from high point of floor.
4. Tack on shims at low points or shim when attaching cabinets to wall.
5. Mark the outlines of all cabinets on the wall to check actual cabinet dimensions against your layout.

35. A. _____
    B. _____
    C. _____
    D. _____
    E. _____

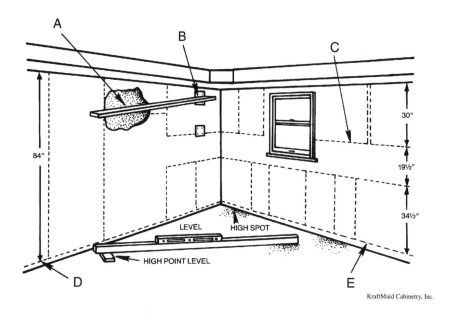

KraftMaid Cabinetry, Inc.

UNIT 20

Painting, Finishing, and Decorating

Text Pages 557-577

Name _____

Date _____ Score _____

1. Refer to the illustration below and name the different types of paintbrushes.

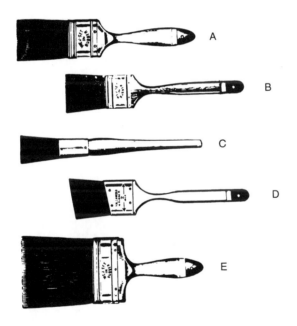

1. A. _____

   B. _____

   C. _____

   D. _____

   E. _____

2. Identify the specified parts of the paintbrush illustrated below.

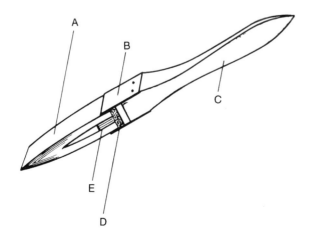

2. A. _____

   B. _____

   C. _____

   D. _____

   E. _____

3. The purpose of the plug in a paintbrush is to _____.
   A. save on the number of bristles in the brush
   B. create a void that will hold a supply of paint
   C. provide a base for attaching bristles

3. _____

4. The _____ type of paint sprayer uses the same principle of operation as an atomizer.

4. _____

5. _(A)_ and _(B)_ sanders are best for smoothing of wood surfaces to be painted or varnished.

5. A. _____

   B. _____

6. Spirit stains have either _(A)_ or _(B)_ as their base.

6. A. _____

   B. _____

7. Why is sandpaper sometimes used between coats of varnish or clear sealer? Select best answer.

7. _____

   A. To smooth previously coated surface.
   B. To provide a slightly roughened surface for better adhesion of the next coat.
   C. To reduce grain raise.

8. _____ is the lightness or darkness of a color.

8. _____

9. The illustration below shows a grid of expanded metal placed in a paint container. Its purpose is to _____.

9. _____

   A. flatten the nap of a roller so paint won't spatter
   B. provide a place to strike off excess paint from a brush or roller
   C. place a "pattern" on the roller that will be transferred to the surface being painted

Name _____

10. Extremely weathered exterior wood surfaces must be sanded to bright wood before being repainted. True or False?

10. _____

11. Alkyds and water-based paints require more brushing than oil paints. True or False?

11. _____

12. A dent in a surface being stained and varnished should be removed before beginning to stain. A small dent may be raised by applying a small amount of _____.

12. _____

    A. water
    B. alcohol
    C. shellac

13. A painted surface develops blisters and begins to peel within a year after application. The probable cause is _____.

13. _____

    A. inferior paint lacking in elasticity
    B. water under the coating pushing the film away from the wood surface
    C. the use of too little oil in the paint
    D. the formation of mildew

14. Using the following information, figure out how much paint will be required to cover the walls of a 12′ × 14′ room with 8′ ceilings. The windows and doors take up 48 sq. ft. and the paint coverage is 400 sq. ft. per gallon. Two coats will be applied. (Make your calculations in the space below.)

14. _____

UNIT 21

Chimneys and Fireplaces

Text Pages 581-594

Name _____

Date _____ Score _____

1. Masonry chimneys are usually freestanding, which means they are structurally separated from the building frame. Footings should extend below the frost line and project at least __(A)__ beyond the sides. When a flue lining is used, the minimum recommended thickness of the chimney wall should be __(B)__.

2″	6″
3″	8″
4″	10″

1. A. _____

   B. _____

2. Building codes require that chimneys be constructed high enough to avoid downdrafts caused by the turbulence of wind. In the illustration below, provide the minimum recommended height for each chimney shown.

2. A. _____

   B. _____

   C. _____

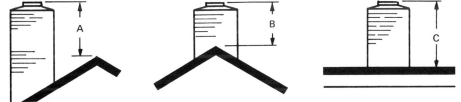

3. The drawing below shows a cross section of a chimney surrounded by typical framing. The framing should clear the masonry by a minimum distance of __(A)__. When two flues adjoin each other as shown, the joints of the flue lining should be offset vertically a minimum distance of __(B)__.

3. A. _____

   B. _____

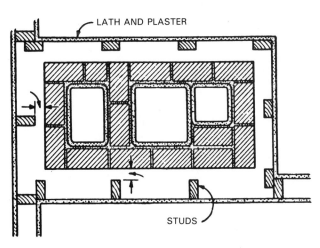

LATH AND PLASTER

STUDS

4. The National Building Code specifies that the wall thickness of fireclay flue linings be no less than _____ thick.

    A. 1/2″
    B. 5/8″
    C. 3/4″
    D. 7/8″

4. _____

5. The area of passage (inside cross section) of a 12 × 16 modular flue liner is listed as 120 sq. in. If it were necessary to substitute a round liner for the 12 × 16 modular liner, what size should be selected to provide about the same area of passage? (Make your calculations in the space below.)

    A. 10″ dia.
    B. 12″ dia.
    C. 15″ dia.
    D. 18″ dia.

5. _____

6. When offsets or bends are necessary in a masonry chimney, the flue lining should be carefully mitered and fitted. The angle of the bend should never exceed _____ with a vertical line or plane.

    A. 30°
    B. 45°
    C. 55°
    D. 60°

6. _____

7. Chimneys are often enlarged just before they project through the roof. This enlargement, obtained by a laying operation called corbeling, should extend downward from the roof framing by a distance not less than _____.

    A. 2″
    B. 4″
    C. 6″
    D. 8″

7. _____

8. The drawing below shows a section view of a standard masonry fireplace. Identify the parts as specified.

8. A. _____

    B. _____

    C. _____

    D. _____

    E. _____

    F. _____

    G. _____

Name _____

9. The _____ is the part of a fireplace in which the ashes are collected and stored for later removal.

9. _____

10. The steel member ordinarily placed across the top of the fireplace opening to support further masonry construction is called a(n) _____.

10. _____

    A. angle iron
    B. lintel
    C. head jamb
    D. header

11. The front opening of a conventional fireplace usually ranges in width from 28″ to 40″. Although the height of the opening may vary considerably, the usual size is from _____.

11. _____

    A. 18″ to 24″
    B. 20″ to 26″
    C. 28″ to 30″
    D. 30″ to 36″

12. The side and back walls of the fireplace (where the fire is located) must be lined with firebrick up to the level of the __(A)__. The firebrick must be set in a special clay mortar. The total thickness of the walls, including the firebrick, should not be less than __(B)__.

12. A. _____

    B. _____

    6″
    8″
    9″
    10″

13. The sidewalls of a standard fireplace are usually constructed at an angle, mainly for the purpose of reflecting heat into the room. This angle is normally laid out at about _____.

13. _____

    A. 3″ per ft.
    B. 4″ per ft.
    C. 5″ per ft.
    D. 6″ per ft.

14. The passageway between the combustion chamber (main fireplace) and the smoke chamber is called a throat. Its cross-sectional area should be equal to that of the flue and it should have a vertical height of about _____.

14. _____

    A. 4″ to 6″
    B. 6″ to 8″
    C. 8″ to 10″
    D. 10″ to 12″

15. When installing a damper unit, a clearance should be provided at each end to allow for _____.

15. _____

    A. soot buildup
    B. free operation
    C. insulation
    D. expansion

16. All surfaces of the smoke chamber should be plastered with a coat of cement mortar to a minimum thickness of _____.

    A. 3/8″
    B. 1/2″
    C. 5/8″
    D. 3/4″

16. _____

17. One recommended method of calculating the cross-sectional area for a fireplace flue is to allow _____ for every square foot of the fireplace opening.

    A. 7 sq. in.
    B. 9 sq. in.
    C. 11 sq. in.
    D. 13 sq. in.

17. _____

18. A somewhat _____ (larger, smaller) flue may be required in chimneys lower than 20′.

18. _____

19. The purpose of the smoke shelf is to redirect the downdraft of the chimney. It should be made equal to or longer than the damper unit, and no less than _____ in depth (width).

    A. 4″
    B. 6″
    C. 8″
    D. 10″

19. _____

20. The use of a metal built-in circulator will increase the heating efficiency of a fireplace. Standard models are designed in about the same way as a regular masonry fireplace. They include a combustion chamber, throat, damper, smoke shelf, and _____.

20. _____

21. Wood trim members are often used around a fireplace opening. According to FHA specifications, wooden parts should not be placed closer than _____ to the side edges of the opening.

    A. 3 1/2″
    B. 4 1/2″
    C. 5 1/2″
    D. 6 1/2″

21. _____

Name _____

22. A prefabricated fireplace is shown in the illustration below. Cultured stone has been used to finish the wall surface. From the following statements concerning this type of fireplace, select the one that is *incorrect*.

    22. _____

    A. Warm air is fed into the room from grillwork along the bottom edge.
    B. A blower may be used to increase the flow of air through the fireplace.
    C. Air for combustion is provided through a duct running to the outside.

23. Free-standing fireplaces are usually constructed with double walls. The smoke pipe running to the ceiling is usually _____.

    23. _____

    A. single-walled
    B. double-walled
    C. triple-walled

24. A boxlike structure, built either inside or outside the regular framing to hold the fireplace or chimney system, is called a(n) _____.

    24. _____

UNIT 22

Post-and-Beam Construction

Text Pages 595-610

Name _____

Date _____ Score _____

1. Post-and-beam construction consists of three basic framing members. Identify each item specified in the drawing below.

1. A. _____

    B. _____

    C. _____

    D. _____

    E. _____

2. An important advantage of post-and-beam construction over standard wood framing or frames consisting of metal beams is its high _____ factor.

2. _____

3. Beams are often joined by butting them together and locating the joint over a post. The bearing surface of the post should be increased by attaching _____ or using a heavy steel plate.

    A. angle irons
    B. beam hangers
    C. bearing blocks
    D. metal straps

3. _____

4. When posts extend upward a considerable distance without lateral bracing, they must have adequate cross-sectional area to prevent buckling. Requirements are usually listed as a l/d ratio. Determine the l/d ratio for a 4×4 solid post that is 10′ long. Round out your answer to the nearest whole number. (Make your calculations in the space below.)

4. _____

5. Determine the l/d ratio for a 6 × 6 solid post that is 14′ long. Round out your answer to the nearest whole number. (Make your calculations in the space below.)

5. _____

6. Beams may consist of solid wood or may be built up in various ways. Identify the types of beams shown in cross-sectional views below.

6. A. _____

   B. _____

   C. _____

   D. _____

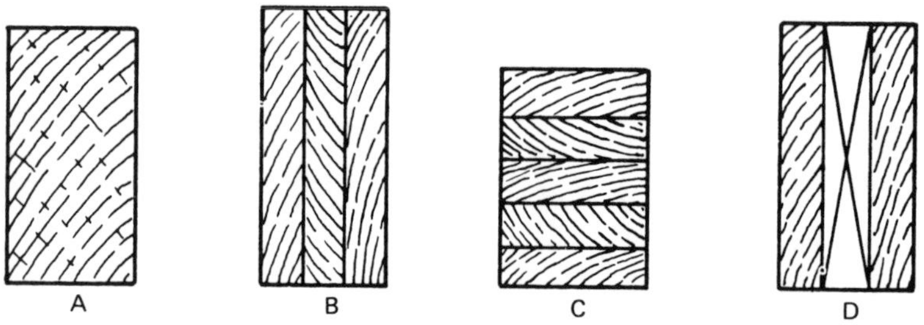

7. Posts are usually spaced evenly along the length of the structure. To take full advantage of modular materials, the spacing should be based on standard increments of _____, 24″, and 48″.

   A. 16″
   B. 18″
   C. 20″
   D. 30″

7. _____

8. Typical sill construction used for a post-and-beam frame is shown in the illustration below. Identify the parts specified.

8. A. _____

   B. _____

   C. _____

   D. _____

   E. _____

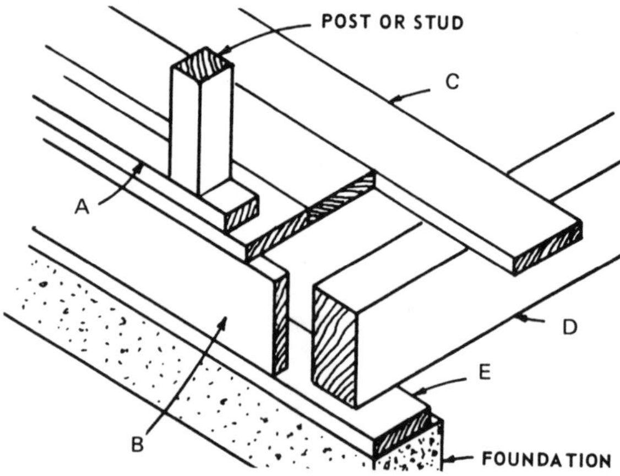

9. There are two basic types of roof beams. A transverse beam runs in the same direction as a common rafter. The other type runs parallel to the supporting side walls and is called a _____ beam.

9. _____

Name _____

10. A post-and-beam frame consists of a limited number of joints. Metal connections are often used to reinforce these joints. To increase the holding power of metal connectors, they should be attached with bolts or _____.

10. _____

11. Full-height partitions are somewhat more difficult to construct in post-and-beam frames. A partition that runs parallel to a transverse beam will have a _____ top plate.

11. _____

    A. staggered
    B. horizontal
    C. supporting
    D. sloping

12. Special framing or support _____ (is, is not) required when nonbearing partitions run parallel to the floor planks.

12. _____

13. Planks for floor or roof decks usually have a tongue-and-groove edge and are sometimes end matched. Standard thicknesses vary from _____.

13. _____

    A. 1 1/2″ to 3″
    B. 2″ to 3″
    C. 2″ to 4″
    D. 2″ to 4 1/2″

14. In cold climates, plank roof structures located directly over heated areas require the same considerations as those applied to outside walls. Identify the items specified in the drawing below.

14. A. _____
    B. _____
    C. _____
    D. _____

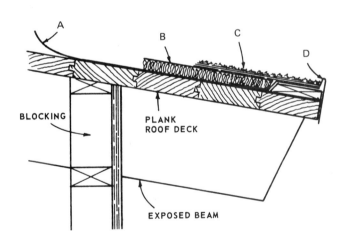

BLOCKING

PLANK ROOF DECK

EXPOSED BEAM

15. The view below shows prefabricated panels being used to form a roof deck. They were made by pressure-gluing 3/8″ plywood to both sides of 2 × 4 framing. Prefabricated components of this type are referred to as _____ panels.

15. _____

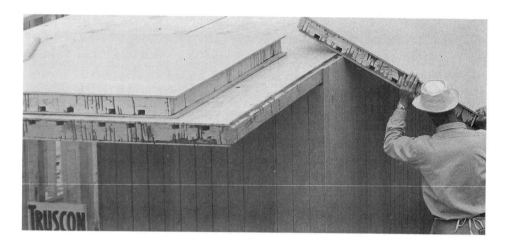

16. Prefabricated units consisting of a foamed polystyrene or paper honeycomb core instead of the 2 × 4 framing are called _____ panels.

16. _____

17. In modern construction, box beams made of plywood webs are often used because of their high strength-to-weight ratio. They can be designed to span distances up to _____.

17. _____

    A. 60′
    B. 80′
    C. 100′
    D. 120′

18. Laminated wood beams and arches are usually made from layers of _____ (hardwood, softwood) glued together with waterproof adhesives.

18. _____

19. In residential construction, laminated beams are generally straight or tapered. In institutional or commercial buildings, however, they are often formed into curves, arches, and other shapes. Provide the correct name for the standard forms shown below.

19. A. _____
    B. _____
    C. _____
    D. _____
    E. _____
    F. _____

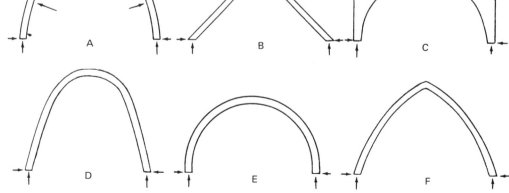

Name _____

20. When fabricating long lengths of laminated arches and beams (see illustration below), it is usually necessary to join the ends of pieces that make up a given layer. A special finger joint is commonly used. These joints should be staggered at least _____ in adjacent layers.

20. _____

    A. 16″
    B. 24″
    C. 32″
    D. 36″

UNIT 23

Systems-Built Housing

Text Pages 611-626

Name _____

Date _____ Score _____

1. In modern construction, the terms "systems-built" and "factory-built" refer to the cutting and assembly of parts, sub-assemblies, and sections in plants and factories. These units are then transported to the _____ _____ for final assembly and erection.

1. _____

2. Below is a view inside a component plant. It shows a nailing machine in operation. The part being nailed consists of two 2″ × 12″ pieces with a 1/2″ spacer. It will be part of a wall frame and is called a(n) _____.

2. _____

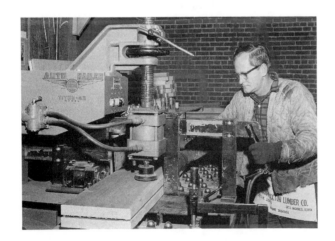

3. Roof trusses are widely used in modern construction. High production rates can be attained in fabricating this building component by cutting the members to length on a _____ saw.

3. _____

    A. movable table
    B. radial arm
    C. double-end
    D. swinging cutoff

4. Today, a large percentage of residential structures and other small buildings are prefabricated in manufacturing plants. Basically, there are five types of prefabricated buildings. Match the correct term with the brief descriptions below.

    A. Flat sections of the structure are fabricated on assembly lines.
    B. All lumber is cut to length and labeled.
    C. Entire units are assembled and finished both inside and outside.
    D. The floor frame is attached to a steel chassis.
    E. Logs are precut and stacked.

4. Modular: _____
   Precut: _____
   Manufactured
     home: _____
   Log home: _____
   Panelized: _____

5. The illustration below shows a large hydraulic press being used to install connectors. What is the correct name of the building component being fabricated?

5. _____

6. In modern prefabrication plants, the various members of a roof truss are usually assembled with _____ connectors.

    A. split-ring
    B. gang-nail
    C. gusset-plate
    D. T-bolt

6. _____

7. The illustration below shows the erection of a factory-built home. This type of prefabrication is generally known as _____.

7. _____

WAUSAW HOMES INC.

8. In manufacturing plants, wall panel frames are assembled by placing the studs, headers, and plates in positioning _____ and then fastening them together with power nailers.

8. _____

Name _____

9. Closed panels, such as the one pictured here, may have voids called _____ or _____ through which electrical wiring or plumbing pipes are run.

9. _____
   _____

ENERCEPT, INC.

10. In the view below, a gang of power nailers are being used to secure plywood sheathing to an outside wall frame. The nailers are powered with _____.

10. _____

   A. compressed air
   B. electricity
   C. hydraulic fluid

11. In panelized prefabrication, a minimum amount of on-site labor is required to complete the structure. Which of the following statements is *incorrect* concerning this type of construction?

11. _____

   A. Most of the wall, ceiling, and floor surfaces are finished in the plant.
   B. Kitchen cabinets can be installed before the section leaves the plant.
   C. Plumbing fixtures are seldom installed until erection is completed on the building site.
   D. Transportation problems limit the maximum width of any given section.

12. A section which includes a concentration of heating and plumbing facilities is shown in the illustration below. This type of section is often included in a prefabrication system that consists mainly of panels. The section is generally referred to as a _____.

12. _____

13. Manufactured homes (formerly called mobile) are generally defined as a trailer equipped for living that is over 28′ long and weighing over _____.

13. _____

    A. 4000 lb.
    B. 4500 lb.
    C. 5000 lb.
    D. 5500 lb.

14. The sidewalls of the mobile home illustrated in the exploded view below are constructed with _____ studs.

14. _____

    A. 1×3
    B. 2×2
    C. 2×3
    D. 2×4

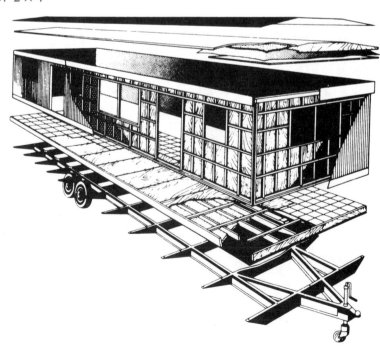

UNIT 24

Passive Solar Construction

Text Pages 627-642

Name _____

Date _____ Score _____

1. Solar construction is based upon the known fact that _____ moves from warmer space to cooler space.

1. _____

2. Look at the illustration below and indicate which of the following statements is *not* true.

2. _____

    A. Heat from solar radiation cannot pass through glass.

    B. Solar radiation can pass through glass much easier than heat.

    C. Solar radiation and the heat it generates differ in ability to pass through glazing. The difference is a heat buildup known as the "greenhouse effect."

    D. The temperature inside the automobile shown will be greater than the temperature outside.

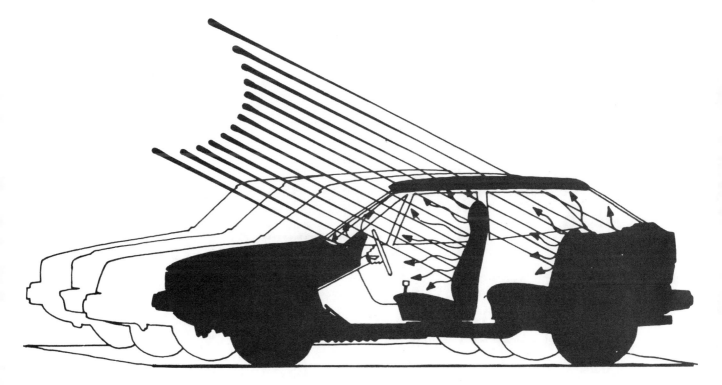

3. The illustration below shows a typical passive solar design. Identify the type.   3. _____

    A. indirect gain
    B. direct gain
    C. isolated gain or sunspace

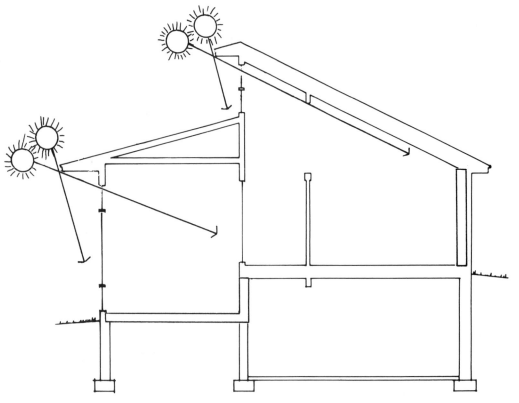

4. The illustration below is an example of a(n) _____ (active, passive) solar design.   4. _____

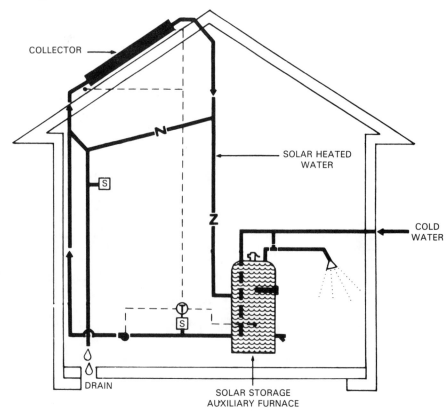

Name _____

5. A simple isolated gain solar system is shown below. Identify the labeled parts of the structure.

5. A. _____

B. _____

C. _____

D. _____

E. _____

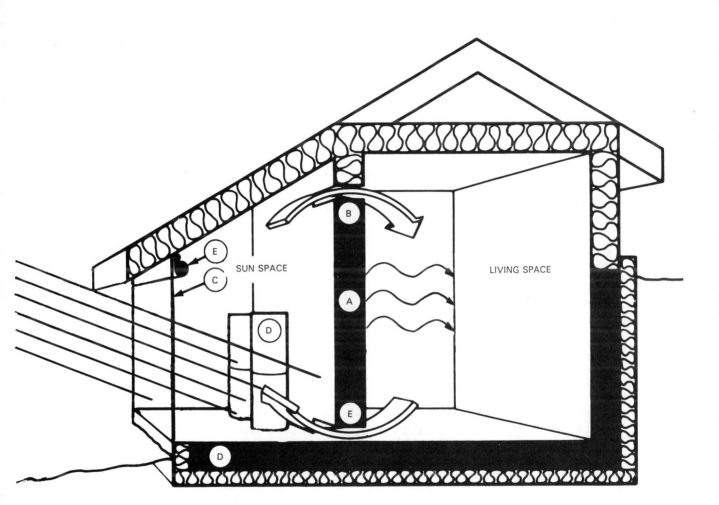

SUN SPACE

LIVING SPACE

6. Which of the following are *not* disadvantages of a passive solar construction?

A. Temperature swings (high to low) are as much as 10° to 15°.
B. It is difficult to control heat and its movement inside the dwelling.
C. System is expensive to maintain.
D. System will not work during a power outage.

6. _____

7. List three methods of heat control for passive solar structures in the summertime.

7. A. _____

B. _____

C. _____

8. Compute to the nearest full inch, the amount of overhang needed to shade a south-facing window in northern Minnesota until August 1. The vertical distance from the bottom of the glass to the underside of the overhang is 9′. Use the chart on page 634 of the text. (Make your calculations in the space below.)

8. _____

9. The proper factor for determining width of a shading overhang is determined by the latitude of the structure. To find the overhang for a central Florida home that will provide shading through August 1, you must use a factor of

9. _____

_____.

   A. 11.1
   B. 6.3
   C. 5.6
   D. 4.5

10. _____ _____ is effectively used to reduce nighttime loss of heat through glass.

10. _____

11. The first step in solar construction is to _____.

11. _____

   A. dig footings for the Trombe wall
   B. determine if there is enough sunshine to make solar construction worthwhile
   C. determine the size of your glazing
   D. locate the garage
   E. locate the structure so the south wall will catch the sun's rays all day long

12. Location of the structure to receive maximum advantage of solar heating is called _____.

12. _____

   A. balancing
   B. orientation
   C. sizing

13. Triple _____ are not generally recommended for passive systems since they reduce the effectiveness of solar radiation.

13. _____

14. For best balance of solar and internal heat, it is best to locate heat generating activities in the _____ side of the residence.

14. _____

Name _____

15. When building a masonry wall for storage of solar heat, thickness of the wall is important. If the wall is too thin, it will deliver its heat too soon and the wall will have cooled before morning. A suitable thickness for a brick wall is _____.

15. _____

    A. 6″ to 10″
    B. 8″ to 12″
    C. 10″ to 14″

16. In some passive systems, collected solar heat is moved by ducts and stored in rock bins (see illustration below). It is important that these be properly sized. Compute the volume of rock storage for a collector area of 250 sq. ft. Refer to text page 640 and make your calculations. (Make your calculations in the space below.)

16. _____

(Iowa Energy Policy Council)

UNIT 25

Remodeling, Renovating, and Repairing

Text Pages 643-665

Name _____

Date _____ Score _____

1. Following is a list of some of the jobs that must be done to renovate the exterior of an old house. Place them in a logical order.

    A. Repair or replace windows.
    B. Repair or replace siding.
    C. Repair or replace the roof.
    D. Perform all structural work, proceeding from the bottom up.
    E. Stain or prime wood siding.
    F. Paint.
    G. Caulk, glaze and putty.
    H. Regrade site and provide drainage away from the house.

1. _____

_____

_____

_____

_____

_____

_____

_____

2. Describe what is being done in the illustration below.

_____

_____

_____

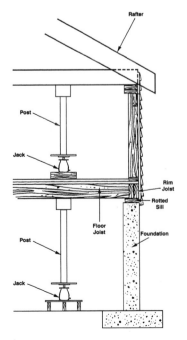

3. When remodeling requires changes in the structure of a building, the carpenter should attempt to _____ the type of framing originally used.

3. _____

4. Older homes usually have a balloon frame. In this type of framing, studs run from the sill to the plate that supports the rafters. Identify the parts of a balloon frame as specified below.

4. A. _____

    B. _____

    C. _____

    D. _____

    E. _____

    F. _____

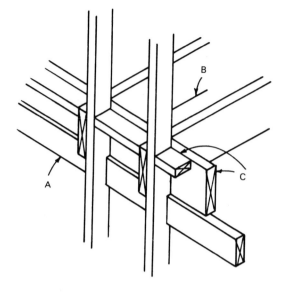

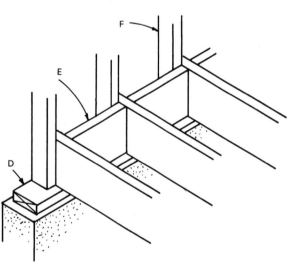

5. When the remodeling work will include excavating, the plans should include the location of _____ utility services.

5. _____

6. For the rapid removal of lath and drywall, many carpenters use a _____.

6. _____

    A. reciprocating saw
    B. garden spade
    C. rip chisel
    D. wrecking bar

Name _____

7. Shoring must be erected before removing a bearing wall. Which one of the
   following *is not* an indication that the wall is load bearing?   7. _____

    A. Overhead joists are spliced over the wall.
    B. The wall runs parallel to an outside wall.
    C. The wall runs at right angles to overhead joists.
    D. The wall runs down the middle of the building lengthwise.

8. Draw an arrow to each bearing wall in the illustration below.

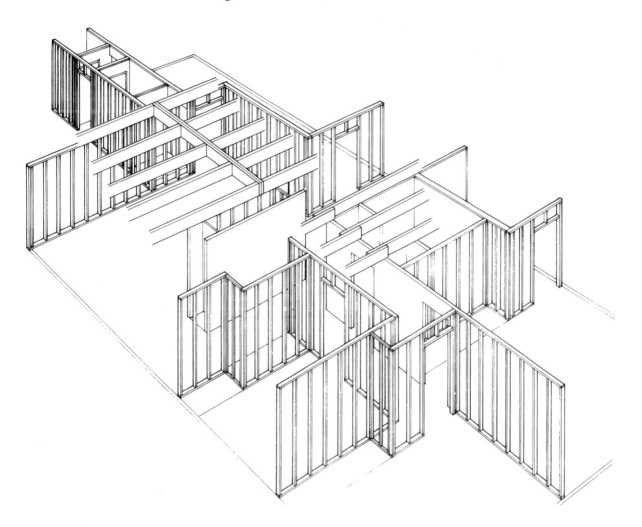

9. Identify the framing members in the following illustration.

9. A. _____

B. _____

C. _____

D. _____

E. _____

F. _____

G. _____

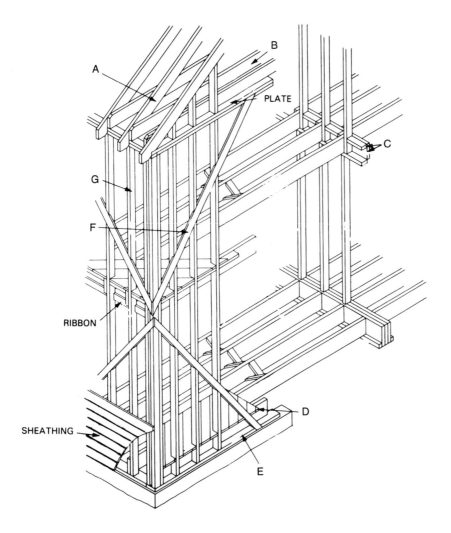

10. Headers are used to carry the load over an opening in a bearing wall. The short studs that support the header are called _____.

10. _____

11. Loads on headers and beams are calculated by using average weights for various areas of a home. Load per square foot for low attic areas is __(A)__. Load per square foot for second floor areas is __(B)__.

11. A. _____

B. _____

Name _____

12. The drawing below shows one method of supporting ceiling joists with a concealed header. The metal devices used for this construction are called _____.

12. _____

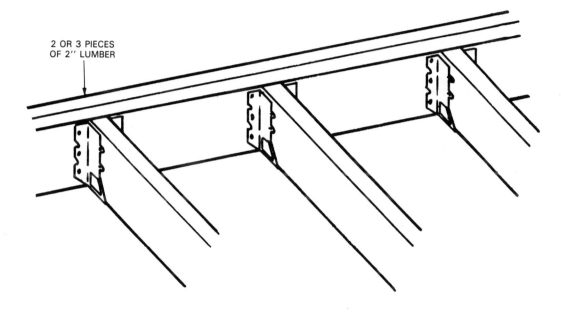

2 OR 3 PIECES
OF 2″ LUMBER

13. The cross-section size of framing members in older homes will not be the same as modern dimension lumber. For example, the size of a 2 × 4 will be slightly _____ (larger, smaller).

13. _____

14. When installing a new nonbearing partition in an existing room, each stud is measured and cut separately. It is then toenailed to the sole and top plate using _____ nails.

14. _____

   A. 6d common
   B. 8d common
   C. 8d box
   D. 10d box

15. Prehung replacement door units (exterior) are designed to save energy. From the list of installation procedures below, select the one that is *incorrect*.

15. _____

   A. Remove the old door, hinges, strike plate, threshold, and frame.
   B. Apply a double bead of caulking along the base of the door opening.
   C. Install screws on the hinge side of the door frame and then on the lock side.
   D. Use long screws that will go through the hinges and into the structural frame.

16. Modern exterior door units are equipped with a combination of magnetic type and compression type weatherstripping. Which one of the following statements is *correct* concerning this installation?

16. _____

    A. Use compression type on top and hinge side.
    B. Use magnetic type on hinge side and top.
    C. Use magnetic type on lock side and top.
    D. Use compression type on lock and hinge side.

17. The cutaway view below shows how a patented jamb clip is used instead of regular blocking. Which one of the following statements is *correct*?

17. _____

    A. Clips are attached to the rough opening and then the door jamb is installed.
    B. Fasten clips to door jamb and then install the assembly in the rough opening.

18. In a direct gain passive solar system, a masonry wall is often used to store heat from the sun. For a large expanse of glass, about _____ of masonry is required for every sq. ft. of south-facing glass.

18. _____

    A. 50 lb.
    B. 100 lb.
    C. 150 lb.
    D. 200 lb.

Name _____

19. Older homes can be retrofitted with structures that will provide a method of collecting solar heat. The illustration shown below shows two adaptations known as _____ units. Either can easily be added to an existing dwelling.   19. _____

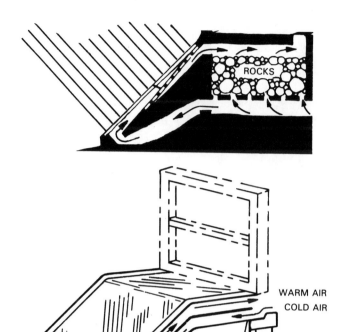

WARM AIR
COLD AIR

20. New OSHA fall regulations allow residential carpenters and contractors to draw up their own fall protection plans. True or False?   20. _____

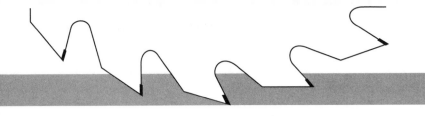

UNIT 26

Electrical Wiring

Text Pages 669-682

Name _____

Date _____ Score _____

1. Study the illustrations below and select the correct answer to the following statement: Electrical wiring should be installed _____ (before, after) the building is insulated.

1. _____

2. The National Electrical Code has the force of law in all municipalities of the United States. True or False?

2. _____

3. A _____ _____ is used to pull individual wires through conduit, but may also be used to pull cable through a wall that is otherwise inaccessible.

3. _____

4. Conductors are _(A)_ in an electrical circuit that carry _(B)_ .

4. A. _____

   B. _____

5. Name the electrical devices shown in the illustrations below.

5. A. _____

   B. _____

   C. _____

   D. _____

   E. _____

A   B   C

Westinghouse

D   E

Pass & Seymour

6. _(A)_ or _(B)_ _____ are electrical devices that protect conductors from overloads by shutting off electrical power to the circuit.

6. A. _____

   B. _____

7. A step-up transformer receives voltage at a higher level and changes it to a lower voltage. True or False?

7. _____

8. The _____ is the conductor that brings electrical power from a transformer to a building.

8. _____

9. Identify the electrical devices represented by the electrical symbols below.

9. A. _____

   B. _____

   C. _____

A   B   C

Name _____

10. Switches are placed only in the _____ of a circuit.   10. _____

    A. hot or black wire
    B. neutral or white wire
    C. ground wire

11. As shown in the illustration below, a neon tester's terminals are inserted in the slots of a receptacle to indicate what?

_____

_____

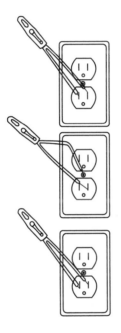

12. If a test shows that there is no electrical current in a receptacle, it always means that the receptacle is faulty. True or False?   12. _____

UNIT 27

Plumbing Systems

Text Pages 683-700

Name _____

Date _____ Score _____

1. Name the five national model plumbing codes.

_____

_____

_____

_____

_____

2. _____ is the part of the drainage piping that allows air to circulate in the drainage pipes.

2. _____

3. Which of the following materials are *not* used for supply pipes and fittings?

    A. Copper.
    B. Galvanized steel.
    C. Malleable iron.
    D. Plastic.

3. _____

4. The two types of plastic used in plumbing supply piping are (use abbreviations) __(A)__ and __(B)__.

4. A. _____

   B. _____

5. Name the types of soil pipe pictured below.

5. A. _____

   B. _____

A

B

6. Identify the parts of the globe valve pictured below.

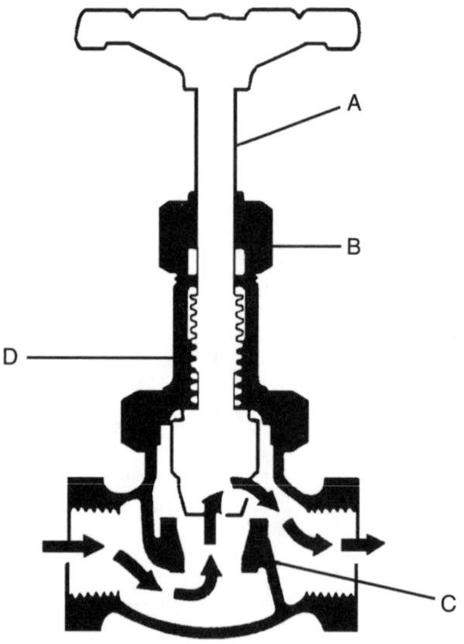

6. A. _____

   B. _____

   C. _____

   D. _____

7. Water using devices in a house are called _____.

7. _____

8. Architectural drawings always include pipe drawings for plumbers to use as a guide to plumbing installations. True or False?

8. _____

9. Compression fittings do not require soldering. True or False?

9. _____

10. To avoid crimping copper tubing while making a bend, a _____ _____ should be used.

10. _____

11. Name the two types of wells commonly used today.

11. _____

_____

12. Name two defects that well water systems develop over time and with constant usage.

_____

_____

13. Name the two methods used to seal joints in hub and spigot soil pipe.

_____

_____

UNIT 28

Heating, Ventilation, and Air Conditioning

Text Pages 701-715

Name _____

Date _____ Score _____

1. Sealing up even small openings in a building conserves energy because _____.

    A. it stops the infiltration of outside air or exfiltration of comfortable conditioned inside air by way of convection currents

    B. the building is sealed against the pressure of wind

    C. cold air cannot enter when the cracks are sealed

    D. cooler conditioned air cannot escape to the outside in hot, humid climates

1. _____

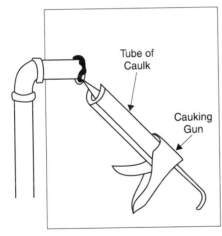

Caulking up joints

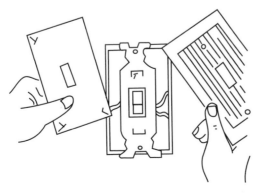

Installing seals behind switch and receptacle plates

2. It is a known physical principal that heat will always migrate to cooler surfaces or environments. What does this tell us about chimneys, windows, and insulation?

_____

_____

3. Identify the specified parts of the gas furnace pictured below.

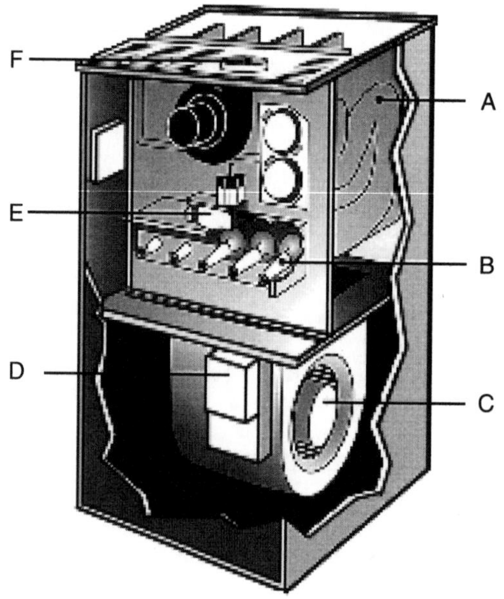

Trane Home Comfort Institute

3. A. _____

   B. _____

   C. _____

   D. _____

   E. _____

   F. _____

4. Which of the following items is *not* a part of a forced air perimeter heating system?

   A. Boiler.
   B. Heat exchanger.
   C. Plenum.
   D. Blower.
   E. Burner.
   F. Ductwork.

4. _____

5. In a forced air heating system, a(n) _____ _____ is a system of ducts that brings cold air back to the furnace from various rooms of the building.

5. _____

6. Name two types of material that are satisfactory for ductwork in a warm air perimeter system.

6. _____

_____

7. A manifold, found in many hydronic heating systems, is used only if _____.

   A. there is an adjusting valve
   B. it is a two-pipe system
   C. it is a one-pipe system
   D. the building has zone heating

7. _____

Name _____

8. Identify the parts of the basic hydronic system shown in the drawing below.

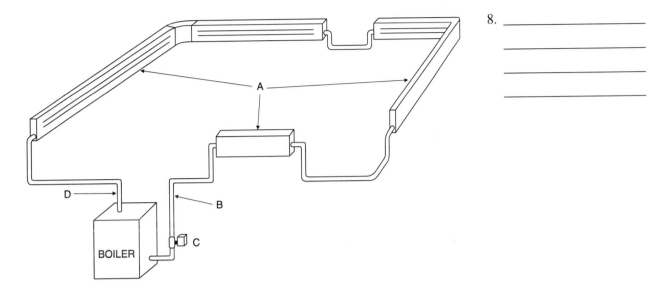

8. _____

_____

_____

_____

9. In an air cooling system, there are two coils through which refrigerant is circulated. One, called a __(A)__, absorbs heat from the warm air passing over it. The heated refrigerant is then pumped through another coil called a __(B)__, where the refrigerant passes its collected heat to the atmosphere.

9. A. _____

B. _____

10. Name the device represented by the drawing below.

10. _____

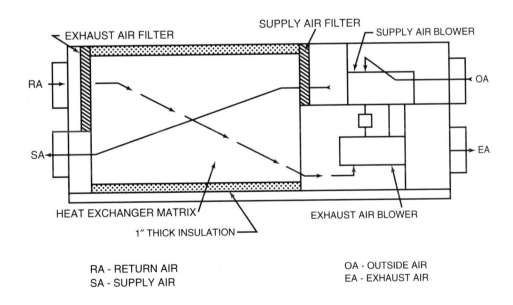

11. Testing has shown that, in a modern home, indoor air should be exchanged
with fresh outdoor air _____.   11. _____
    A. once a day
    B. twice a day
    C. every two to three hours
    D. once a week

UNIT 29

Scaffolds and Ladders

Text Pages 719-728

Name _____

Date _____ Score _____

1. Scaffolding is generally defined as an elevated platform used to support workers, tools, equipment, and __(A)__. One of the prime considerations in its erection or construction is the degree of __(B)__ it will provide.

1. A. _____

   B. _____

2. The height of the platform is important since it must permit the work to be performed with speed and accuracy, without causing unnecessary stooping or _____ by the worker.

2. _____

3. Typical designs for single-pole and double-pole wooden scaffolding are shown in the drawings below. Identify the specified parts.

3. A. _____

   B. _____

   C. _____

   D. _____

   E. _____

   F. _____

   G. _____

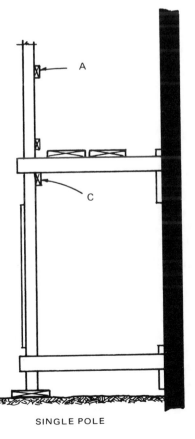

SINGLE POLE

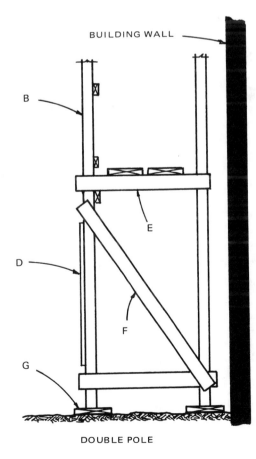

BUILDING WALL

DOUBLE POLE

4. The wood members that support the plank platform should be cut from sound (free of large knots) lumber with a minimum cross section of _____.

    A. 1×6
    B. 2×4
    C. 2×6
    D. 2×8

4. _____

5. In the erection of either single-pole or double-pole scaffolding, ledger sections should never be spaced more than _____ apart.

    A. 8′
    B. 10′
    C. 12′
    D. 14′

5. _____

6. In modern construction, sectional steel or aluminum scaffolds are commonly used. Sections can be rapidly assembled from trussed frames and _____.

6. _____

7. The drawings below show three types of metal devices commonly used in connection with wood planks to form low-level scaffolds. Identify each item shown.

7. A. _____
    B. _____
    C. _____

8. Great care must be exercised when using nails to attach metal scaffolding devices to a wall. Minimum recommendations suggest the use of _____ 16d or 20d nails, driven into sound framing lumber.

    A. two
    B. three
    C. four
    D. five

8. _____

9. Metal units commonly used to support low platforms for interior work are called _____ _____. They are attached to a wooden ledger and can be adjusted to several different heights.

9. _____

Name _____

10. Quality ladders are made from clear, straight-grained stock that is carefully seasoned. Two types of ladders commonly used by the carpenter are shown below. Provide the correct name for the ladder on the left and the names of the parts specified on the single ladder.

10. A. _____

    B. _____

    C. _____

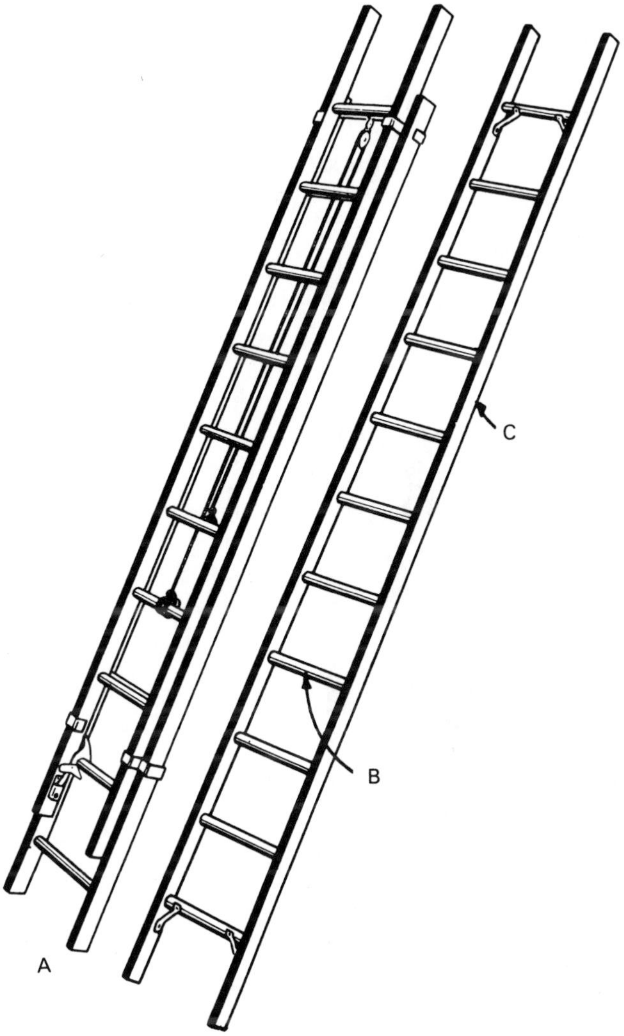

11. When placing a ladder against a wall, the horizontal distance from the lower end to the wall should be at least _____ of the total length of the ladder.

11. _____

    A. 15%
    B. 20%
    C. 25%
    D. 30%

12. When a ladder is used to gain access to a roof it should be long enough to extend above the roof a distance of at least _____.

12. _____

    A. 2 1/2′
    B. 3′
    C. 3 1/2′
    D. 4′

13. Which one of the materials listed below would be best for refinishing a wood ladder or step ladder?

13. _____

    A. Varnish.
    B. Paint.
    C. Enamel.

14. When a ladder is used on surfaces that may permit the bottom end to slip, it is best to _____.

14. _____

    A. nail the rails to anti-skid boards
    B. place the bottom rails of the ladder in a special frame
    C. equip the bottom end of the rails with safety shoes
    D. use a rope to hold the bottom end in place

15. From the list below, select the *incorrect* statement concerning the safe use of the step ladder shown in the view.

15. _____

    A. Do not leave tools on the surface of the top step.
    B. At least three legs should rest on solid support.
    C. Do not stand on the two top steps.
    D. The two sections should be fully opened and locked.

(Patent Scaffold Co.)

16. Never use any type of metal ladder where there is the slightest chance that it might make contact with _____ _____.

16. _____

UNIT 30

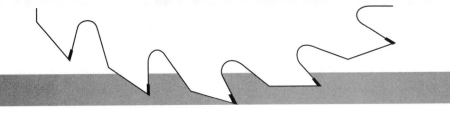

Carpentry—A Career Path

Text Pages 729-738

Name _____

Date _____ Score _____

1. Well over _____ jobs in carpentry are expected to be available on a yearly basis, making this the largest demand area in all the crafts group.

1. _____

2. Since skilled carpenters (journeymen) are capable of performing a variety of work on a regular construction site, they can usually fill the requirements for a broad range of related work. From the following list, select the task which a skilled carpenter *would not* likely be able to handle without additional training.

2. _____

   A. Remodeling and expansion projects on existing structures.
   B. General repair and maintenance work in commercial and institutional buildings.
   C. Heating, plumbing, and electrical maintenance in commercial buildings.
   D. Skilled positions in millwork plants and factories that produce prefabricated structures.

3. In high school, a student who is interested in becoming a carpenter should take as many wood and building construction courses as possible. In addition to other shop courses (metal, electricity, etc.), it is especially important to select one or two courses in the area of _____.

3. _____

4. Students enrolled in vocational-technical schools who are interested in becoming carpenters should take basic courses in _____.

4. _____

   A. concrete work and bricklaying
   B. heating and plumbing
   C. electrical wiring
   D. All of the above areas.

5. The origin of our modern apprenticeship training program can be found in the _____ relationship where the knowledge and skill of a trade was passed along to succeeding generations.

5. _____

   A. master-servant
   B. master-helper
   C. child-parent
   D. craftsperson-laborer

6. During the early period of apprenticeship, the apprentice usually lived in the master carpenter's household and received training over a time span as long as _____.

    A. 4 years
    B. 5 years
    C. 6 years
    D. 7 years

6. _____

7. When training was complete and the master felt that the apprentice had attained a high level of skill, the apprentice was granted the status of _____, and could then work for wages.

7. _____

8. Today, apprenticeship training programs are carefully organized and supervised. Local committees representing labor and _____ provide direct control.

8. _____

9. At the national level, the apprenticeship committee for carpenters includes representatives from the United Brotherhood of Carpenters and Jointers of America, National Association of Home Builders, and the _____.

    A. Better Business Bureau of the United States
    B. Contractor and Laborers Association of America
    C. Associated General Contractors of America, Inc.
    D. Master Builders and Contractors of America

9. _____

10. Applicants for apprentice training programs in carpentry must be at least _____ old and must satisfy the local committee that they have the ability to master the trade.

    A. 16 years
    B. 17 years
    C. 18 years
    D. 19 years

10. _____

11. The term of apprenticeship for carpentry is normally _____, but may be reduced for applicants who have completed advanced courses in vocational-technical schools.

    A. 2 years
    B. 3 years
    C. 4 years
    D. 5 years

11. _____

12. In addition to instruction and skills learned on the job, an apprentice must attend classes in subjects related to carpentry. Classes are usually held in the evening and must total _____ per year.

    A. 72 hr.
    B. 108 hr.
    C. 120 hr.
    D. 144 hr.

12. _____

Name _____

13. Today, an apprentice is an employed worker on the job. The wage scale is determined by the local apprenticeship committee and usually starts at about _____ of the journeyman's scale during the past year.　　13. _____

    A. 40%
    B. 45%
    C. 50%
    D. 55%

14. When the apprenticeship training period is complete and the apprentices have passed a final exam, they are issued a certificate stating that they are _____ carpenters. This certificate is recognized throughout the country.　　14. _____